2007
Mini Saga Competition

Young Writers
in association with
STAEDTLER

mini
S·A·G·A·S·

Fiction From the UK

First published in Great Britain in 2007 by
Young Writers, Remus House, Coltsfoot Drive,
Peterborough, PE2 9JX
Tel (01733) 890066 Fax (01733) 313524
All Rights Reserved

© Copyright Contributors 2007
SB ISBN 978-1-84431-385-3

Foreword

Young Writers was established in 1991, with the aim of encouraging the children and young adults of today to think and write creatively. Our latest secondary school competition, 'Mini S.A.G.A.S.', posed an exciting challenge for these young authors: to write, in no more than fifty words, a story encompassing a beginning, a middle and an end.
We call this the mini saga.

Mini S.A.G.A.S. Fiction From the UK is our latest offering from the wealth of young talent that has mastered this incredibly challenging form. With such an abundance of imagination, humour and ability evident in such a wide variety of stories, these young writers cannot fail to enthral and excite with every tale.

Contents

Bablake School, Coventry
Christine Goldfinch (14) 13

Bankhead Academy, Aberdeen
Lauren Scobbie (12) 14
Alice Booth (12) 15
Shaun Martin (12) 16
Jonathan Heap (12) 17
Blair Sutherland (12) 18
Aimee Jensen (13) 19
Callum Patterson (13) 20

Bordesley Green Girls' School, Birmingham
Aliyah Begum (15) 21

Brockwell Middle School, Cramlington
Alarna Eke (10) 22
Jasmine Murray (10) 23
Gabriel Ardron (13) 24
Jack Hepple 25
Stephen Heads 26
Daniel Mitchell (12) 27
Victoria Reed 28
Emma Carter 29
Christopher Dickinson (12) 30
Calum Aynsley (12) 31

Jonathan Anderson (12) 32
Rachel Jefferson 33
Kerri Ritchie (12) 34
Hannah Phillips (12) 35
Chloe Bell-Slater (12) 36
Rachel Hildreth (11) 37
Adam Harrington (12) 38
Amy Fecitt (12) 39
Richard Kyle (12) 40
Jamie Chalk (12) 41
Connor Rumble 42
Erin Bowmaker (11) 43

Brooke Weston City Technology College, Corby
Leigh Brown (14) 44
Natalie Robinson (13) 45
Maire Beatty (14) 46
Simone Smyth (14) 47
Kate Wallis (12) 48
Laura Keeble (14) 49
Amy Smith (14) 50
Peter Hutchinson (14) 51
Beth Malloy (14) 52
Lauren Albrecht (14) 53
Rachael Collins (14) 54

Deromi Jessiman (14) 55
Chris McGhee (14) 56
Brendan Farrell (13) 57
Alex Barrowman (14) 58
Kelley Ingram (14) 59
Sasha Wakelin (14) 60
Ryan McGreavey (12) 61
George Cottell (12) 62
Emily Rayner 63
Emily Lynch 64
Jake Stevenson 65
Chris Guiver 66
Leigh Brown 67

Buckie High School, Buckie
Karen Burgess (12) 68
Ryan Munro (11) 69
Kiara Anderson (11) 70
Macauly Flaws (12) 71
Kirstie Redford 72
Keiran Riddoch (11) 73

Burgess Hill School, Burgess Hill
Emma Rogers (17) 74

Craigroyston Community High School, Edinburgh
Leanne Cannon (13) 75
Craig Stevenson (13) 76
Jodie Harkins (14) 77
Tommy Macdonald (13) 78
Dean Jones (13) 79

Keith Marshall (14) 80
Ashley Osborne (13) 81
Laura Cunningham (13) 82
Thomas Graham (13) 83

Flint High School, Flint
Jack Heppleston (12) 84
Bethan Phillips (13) 85
Jessica Parry (12) 86
Charlotte Owen (12) 87
Rochelle Bedford (13) 88
James Roberts (12) 89
Hannah Brown (13) 90
Shaun Jones (15) 91
James Ruby Peart (14) 92
Tayla Handforth (13) 93
Jake Massey (13) 94

Glenlola Collegiate School, Bangor
Shannon Campbell (12) 95
Holly Auld (12) 96
Harriet Gillespie (12) 97
Jessica Berry (12) 98
Hannah Gibson (12) 99
Rebecca Davison (12) 100
Ashleigh Fulton (12) 101
Sarah Bailie (12) 102
Louise Black (12) 103
Holli Burgon (12) 104
Trana-Rebecca Gray (12) 105
Kerry Baird (12) 106

Rachel Bolton (12) 107

**Heolddu Comprehensive School,
Bargoed**
Jessica Broom (12) 108
Danielle Melly (12) 109
Abigail Edwards (12) 110
Olivia Jones (12) 111
Stuart Davies (12) 112
Rachael Pippen (12) 113
William Dunford (13) 114
Kirsty Reynolds (12) 115
Rebecca Ingram-Jones (13) 116
Darren Bookless (13) 117
Carol Smith (14) 118
Jessica Morgan Chipperfield (12) 119
Chloe Davies (12) 120
Annalisse Roberts (13) 121
Harley Duggan (12) 122
Alysha Davies (12) 123
Ashleigh Jones (12) 124
Daniel Jones (12) 125
Jack Chard (12) 126
Grant Sullivan (12) 127
Jamie Cobley (12) 128
Luke Ellaway & Thomas Carter (12) 129
Emma Carter 130
Lacey Price (13) 131
Bethan Jenkins (14) 132
Ben Heatley (14) 133
Menna Bradford (14) 134

Jordan Forbes (14) 135
Gary Pine (14) 136
Chantelle Davies (14) 137
Jack Thompson (14) 138
Natasha Muller (14) 139

John Masefield High School, Ledbury
Anton Mizen (13) 140
Peter Foster (14) 141
George Banner (13) 142
Parisa Saberi (13) 143
Becky Brown (13) 144
Connor Bufton (14) 145
Katy Layton (14) 146
Jack Vernall (14) 147
Hannah Bowring (14) 148
Alice Perrett (14) 149
Ellen Jones (14) 150
Kayleigh Pugh (14) 151
Ben Adams (14) 152
Emily Fleck (14) 153
Scott Lincoln (14) 154
Tom Parsons (14) 155
Naomi Parry (14) 156
Sarah Brown (14) 157
Olly Davies-Hodges (14) 158
Tony Foster (14) 159
Elizabeth Williams (14) 160
Seana Russell (13) 161
Brittany Dance (13) 162
Jed Yaxley (13) 163

Adam Paske (12)... 164
Charlotte Firth (12) 165
Kane Weir (13) 166
Kieran Phillips (13)... 167
Mike Green (13)... 168
Steven Rawle (12).. 169
Alice Leaper (12) 170
Gemma Impey (13) 171
Terry Smith (13).. 172
Kamal Morgan (13).. 173
Daniel Garside (14) 174
Leanne Vina (14)... 175
Tiffany Ryder (14).. 176
Ashley Gillespie (14)....................................... 177
Katie Brown (14)... 178
Jed Parry (13).. 179
Abbi Davies (13).. 180
David Benhenni (13)....................................... 181
Sam Keetch (13).. 182
Adam Perks (13).. 183
Ellen Webb (13)... 184
Hayley Jones (13)... 185
Jordan-Leigh Parry (13) 186
Nicholas Hetherington (12)............................. 187
Charlotte Febery (13) 188

King Williams' College, Isle of Man
Caitriona Cox (13)... 189
Jenny Green (16) 190
Kathryn Sharpe (15) 191
Sophie White (13).. 192

Sophie Van Hooven (13).................................. 193
Alex Beadle (14) 194
Harriet Nuttall (13).. 195
Georgie Leece Drinkwater (13)...................... 196
Eleanor Leece Drinkwater (15)....................... 197
Stephanie Carter (13)..................................... 198
Jack Cooper (13) 199
Matt Kneen (13) 200
Grace Harrison (12) 201
Louis Schwalbert (14)..................................... 202
Rowena Farrant (12) 203

Pattison College, Coventry
Grace McCarthy (12) 204

Roseberry School for Girls, Epsom
Lucy Parker (12).. 205

St Mary's School, Gerrards Cross
Georgina Goodgame (14)................................ 206
Soffia Kristinsdottir (13)................................. 207
Hannah Beattie (13) 208
Emily Patching (14).. 209
Danielle Chauhan (14).................................... 210
Jeena Patel (14)... 211
Charlotte Grahame (14)................................. 212
Marie-Claire Giel (14) 213
Megan Brown (14)... 214
Prue Heywood (14).. 215
Parisa Dezfulli (14).. 216
Jessica Cahill (14).. 217
Julia Wessels (13) 218

Rachael Brooks (13) 219
Rebekah Stokes (13)...................... 220
Hannah Caraco (13) 221
Shereen Sagoo (13) 222
Felicity Davis (13) 223
Tara Hurst (13) 224
Lucy Marshall (12) 225

**Sutton Coldfield Grammar School for
Girls, Sutton Coldfield**
Tara Manjunath (13) 226
Aleaza Raheel (13) 227
Frances Hancock (13) 228
Ajit Kaur Sagoo (13) 229
Laura Sumner (13)......................... 230
Imogen Pallister (13)...................... 231
Diana Shiner (12)........................... 232
Anjeevan Klair (13) 233
Chloe Scott (13) 234
Sarah Rehman (13) 235
Anna Owen (13)............................ 236
Laura Bull (12) 237
Chloé Thompson-Haynes (13) 238
Shannan Cox (12) 239
Laurel Windsor (13) 240
Jamilah Campbell (13) 241
Charlotte Baxter (12) 242
Aisha Kaleem (13).......................... 243
Nafeesa Mehmood (13)................... 244
Anmol Hussain (13) 245
Ciara Ryan (13)............................. 246

Shelly Rajput (13)........................... 247
Catherine White (14) 248
Sarah Lyons (14) 249
Sarah Hemming (14)....................... 250
Elizabeth Parry (14) 251
Kate Densley (14).......................... 252
Eleanor Smithson (14) 253
Nicola Swales (14).......................... 254
Rhia Abukhalil (12) 255
Noor Hashim Hussain (11)............... 256
Charlotte Dixon (12)...................... 257
Bethany Holt (12) 258
Hayley Prichard-Jones (12)............................. 259
Dayna Hill (12) 260
Serena Chandra (12) 261
Chloè Upston (12).......................... 262
Allie Hexley (12)............................ 263
Charlotte Heath (12)...................... 264
Vanisha Chauhan (12) 265
Megan Kirby (12)........................... 266
Grace Davis (12)............................ 267
Amber Cruise (12) 268
Stephanie Sam (12)........................ 269
Hajrah Zafar (12)........................... 270
Jasmin Beckford (12) 271
Priya Padham (12).......................... 272
Charanveer Mudher (12)................. 273
Devinia Solanki (11)....................... 274
Charlotte Ridout (12)..................... 275
Shaista Malik (12).......................... 276
Anisa Hawa (12) 277

Nicole Parsons (12) 278
Amy Curry (12) 279
Caryss Jones (11) 280
Bethan Renwick (12) 281
Kirpal Sagoo (12) 282
Constance Martin (12) 283
Stephanie Doswell (12) 284
Maaria Ashraf (12) 285
Elin Lee (12) 286
Hannah Skelding (12) 287
Megan Rowley (12) 288
Jeevan Gogna (12) 289

The Buchan School, Isle of Man
Lily Westerman (11) 290
Sarah Butler (11) 291

Varndean School, Brighton
Yasmin & Sam 292
Emma Hodges 293
Julia Knight 294
Sophie Hyland-Ward 295
Bradley Mitten 296
Amy Jenner (13) 297
Callum Clark (13) 298
Alice Woodings (13) 299
Charlie Pullen 300
Kieran Benn 301

Vermuyden School, Goole
Kayne Hyde (14) 302
Daniel West (13) 303
Brea Walton (14) 304

Vermuyden School, Goole
Ben Evans (14) 305

The Mini Sagas

The Day I Almost Lost My Best Friend

I was riding in the Olympics; we were coming up to the final jump. It was a triple but I knew we'd make it. Up we flew and over, we were clear but as we landed Poppy fell and died.
I suddenly woke up, it was a horrid dream!

Christine Goldfinch (14)
Bablake School, Coventry

13

My Nightmare

I hit the bottom of the sea violently. I let out a yelp,
but only bubbles emerged. I kicked my legs fiercely,
trying to reach the surface. Something was holding
me back,
I woke up drowned in sweat.

Lauren Scobbie (12)
Bankhead Academy, Aberdeen

14

The Wave

The air was cold and the rain was pelting down like bombs in an air raid. A wisp of hair blew into my face. I tried to reach the bus stop, but the bus sped past, drenching me in a wave of cold water. I had missed the bus again.

Alice Booth (12)
Bankhead Academy, Aberdeen

15

Miracle Life

One day a really old man saw a television advert for 'Miracle Life'. It promised that some people who used it would live longer, so he sent away for some. The very next day he died of food poisoning.

Shaun Martin (12)
Bankhead Academy, Aberdeen

The Plane Crash

I poke my nose into the paper to read about world
disasters and feel comforted that I am safe and happy.
Suddenly there is a bang and a rattle.
The plane goes dark and I see a row of dancing
flames rising around me.

Jonathan Heap (12)
Bankhead Academy, Aberdeen

Evil Chase

At 125mph my Aston Martin was gaining on Jaws
McDuff.
McDuff's tyres slid to a halt at the top of the canyon.
I watched his car flip over the edge.
I had waited a long time for my revenge.
I laughed a satisfied laugh.

Blair Sutherland (12)

Bankhead Academy, Aberdeen

18

My Experience From Hell

I was walking past the graveyard when the sky turned grey. Thunder rumbled in the distance, then lightning struck. I heard scraping noises and in the flashes of light I saw shadows.
I screamed.
The shadows chased me to the river. There was no escape.

Aimee Jensen (13)
Bankhead Academy, Aberdeen

The Hostage

'I'm hit! I'm hit!'
I was running in terror through the forest, shooting
any enemy in sight. At last I could see it; the building
where the hostage was held.
I wiped the paint from my sleeve.
Another successful game of Capture the Flag.

Caffum Patterson (13)
Bankhead Academy, Aberdeen

The Hollow Tree

The branches bent down with sorrow. The shriek shifted in every direction, my heart wept. There was nothing to be seen except the swaying of the tree. The wind echoed through me. I couldn't forget the sound. Growing louder in every turn, looking behind, the hollow tree waited.

Afiyah Begum (15)
Bordesley Green Girls' School, Birmingham

Down Under

I kicked out violently in all directions, I was down under. A shudder went down my spine. Darkness was closing in on me like a closing prison door. My heart was pounding like a wooden drum vibrating. I knew I shouldn't but my eyes were closing, flickering very slowly …

Afarna Eke (10)
Brockwell Middle School, Cramlington

The Disappearance

Ally Green was a sad little girl and always miserable until one day she went out into the garden, walked into some grey mist then disappeared.
Some say she died, others say she ran away but the truth is she is trapped forever in a different world, never to return.

Jasmine Murray (10)
Brockwell Middle School, Cramlington

Armageddon

My ceramite power armour clinked as I walked across the mesh deck of the dropzone. I cocked my 'mark three imperial style bolter' as I climbed aboard my drop pod with the other 9 soldiers. I looked through the observation window, down onto the war torn world of Armageddon.

Gabriel Ardron (13)
Brockwell Middle School, Cramlington

Eye Of The Storm

Crash! Bang!
I heard the roof tiles being viciously swept away by
the category 5 hurricane. I sprinted for cover trying
to find somewhere that hadn't been demolished.
I glimpsed shelter where my family were. They
screamed for me, I ran to them although very pale,
they were relieved.

Jack Heppfe
Brockwell Middle School, Cramlington

Plummeting

'You can't!' I exclaimed as my kidnapper dangled me
over the edge of the cliff by my arm, 'you can't!'
Why couldn't he? What was stopping him? Nothing
was! I found myself plummeting to the choppy seas.
My life flashed past.
To never see my family … Living hell!

Stephen Heads
Brockwell Middle School, Cramlington

Edge Of Disaster

As I barrel-rolled through the darkness of space
in my X-wing: *Bang!* An engine flew straight off. I
started plummeting down towards a planet gaining
speed rapidly.
There wasn't much hope left for me now – debris
flying everywhere. My ship on fire, 'Mayday! Mayday!
Going down …'

Daniel Mitcheff (12)
Brockwell Middle School, Cramlington

27

Isolation

He whimpered and cried, 'Leave me alone!'
But the bully said, 'No!'
He went to the ground with a thud. Battered and
bruised he stumbled the path home.
Next day at school he was alone. 'Ouch!' He was on
the floor again. His body was alive but he felt dead.

Victoria Reed
Brockwell Middle School, Cramlington

Lost

'Where is he?'

The darkness was making it hard to see. I heard a noise so I ran. I'd been looking for hours now. Where could he be? I stopped; there in front me lay bones.

'It can't be?'

I heard a bark. I turned around, there he was …

Emma Carter
Brockwell Middle School, Cramlington

29

The Most Important Match Of My Life

On Sunday I played a game for my football team, Cramlington Juniors. I thought that it would be another game in the league, but this game was different. It was against our archrivals, Wallsend. It was the most important match of my life … did we win?

Christopher Dickinson (12)
Brockwell Middle School, Cramlington

30

The End

They started the rocket. On our way to salvation. The boosters full blast, we're going to Utopia. The last safe place – reality is collapsing but the legendary Utopia Project can save us. But where is it? It doesn't exist. Nothing but the darkness and the cold; just the end …

Calum Aynsley (12)
Brockwell Middle School, Cramlington

Happy Gilmore

Happy Gilmore tees off on the last hole, takes his shot … what a drive! 400 yards, 6 metres from the hole and here comes his rival … Shooter McGavin tees off 320 yards; he shot; 3 metres from the hole. Happy putts; he misses. All goes down to the last shot …

Jonathan Anderson (12)
Brockwell Middle School, Cramlington

32

How Could He?

I just sat there, watching the raindrops drip down the window. How could he do this to us? How could he just walk out and leave us with nothing? I turned around and there he was, standing in the doorway.

'I'm sorry,' he said.

Bang!

I fell to the ground.

Rachel Jefferson
Brockwell Middle School, Cramlington

Bloody Murder

Images awoke me, I sat up; it was true!
She lay there, but where was he? Lying lifeless. I remembered.
Why? Why us? Why her? Why not me? What had he done? It had been her only chance ... what had he used?
The terror remained; etched in her face.

Kerri Ritchie (12)
Brockwell Middle School, Cramlington

Crash, Bang!

Suddenly, *crash, bang!*
Glass smashed to the ground. It stopped. I tiptoed to the bathroom, *crash, bang!* again. Shutting the door; footsteps getting louder and louder. Tension. *What was it? Who was it? What did they want?* All these questions going through my head.
Please! Help me! *Crash, bang!*

Hannah Phillips (12)
Brockwell Middle School, Cramlington

The Littlest Thing

Oh no! They were at it again. Rowing. They always rowed about the smallest things.

That day was no different. That day it was about the washing up.

'Right! I've had enough I'm leaving and never coming back!' yelled Dad.

A week later the papers came through. Divorce papers!

Chloe Bell-Slater (12)

Brockwell Middle School, Cramlington

Stumbling

Stumbling home; streets empty. Meant to be a memorable 'night on the town'. It's a night to remember alright, I've probably broken the world vomiting record! Vodka burning my throat, I continue downing it. I fall onto the road, crying. Headlights come.

Bang!

Stumbling into the last of my life …

Rachel Hildreth (11)
Brockwell Middle School, Cramlington

37

The Demon Bowler

'Ian Botham here and let me say, this is the best
Ashes Series I have ever seen. Here is the youngster,
Adam Harrington: *'The Demon Bowler'*. If he bowls
Ricky Ponting out in this over -
It's a long trip home for Australia.'

Adam Harrington (12)
Brockwell Middle School, Cramlington

Cliffhanger

My brother was driving his friend's truck; taking me
to a party.
Being foggy, we missed the turning, bringing us down
a bumpy road instead. We got to the edge; of a cliff!
Helping each other, we escaped the truck. The cliff
we discovered however, was actually only 2ft down!

Amy Fecitt (12)
Brockwell Middle School, Cramlington

Tickets

Two teenagers; big Newcastle fans, on a mission to get season tickets. They try to earn the money by shoplifting. By stealing, they get how much they need. So, they go to buy the tickets and are overjoyed until they find out they have bought the wrong tickets!

Richard Kyle (12)
Brockwell Middle School, Cramlington

The War

I hear the scream of gunfire. My red-stained uniform.
The wind of death blows. I feel him tap my shoulder.
Death walks here. I beg to be spared. I want to live, I
have more to do in life. I am shot down; just like that.
Bang!

Jamie Chalk (12)
Brockwell Middle School, Cramlington

Mystery Unexplained

As she walked into the cold dripping cave, she couldn't help but feel a shiver go down her spine. She looked below herself, the murder weapon, a rusted knife with blood on the tip. As she stood up, there was the murderer staring at her, copying her every move, mirrored.

Connor Rumble
Brockwell Middle School, Cramlington

42

Death?

I run down the lane thinking, *oh what have I done wrong?* Man running, knife pointing. Am I going to die? I turn my head. To my surprise the man is right there. I feel a pain and then a trickle. *Oh blood! Am I going to die? Death may come swiftly ...*

Erin Bowmaker (11)
Brockwell Middle School, Cramlington

43

It's Alive

In the old street the scrumptious smell of baked goods filled the air. The muffin man was working on his marvellous creation; days and days were spent on making the magnificent creature perfect when … 'Eureka, it's alive,' a vision of gumdrop beauty and gingery goodness with legs of speed. *Wow!*

Leigh Brown (14)
Brooke Weston City Technology College, Corby

44

Midnight

Midnight was approaching. The dark sombre sky
illuminated the sparkling stars in the moonlight.
Silhouettes danced around below the moonlit sky.
Trees swayed smoothly, to the silent beat of the
wind. Houses enclosed communities in the warmth,
but on this chilling night, the darkness was certain to
absorb the existence.

Natalie Robinson (13)
Brooke Weston City Technology College, Corby

Frankenstein (Chapter 5)

One autumn night, Dr Frankenstein brought his creation to life. His drawing was beautiful but the real creation was horrific. He collapsed in his room and woke up from a nightmare with his creation staring at him and smiling with his black lips. Suddenly he leapt up into the night …

Maire Beatty (14)
Brooke Weston City Technology College, Corby

Tears Of Sorrow

Hanging on a cliff edge, this was the end. I stared up at my mother's tear-stained face as she prayed with all of her heart. My hands lost grip and I plunged into the world beneath. I tried to gasp for air, only taking in water. Was this it?

Simone Smyth (14)
Brooke Weston City Technology College, Corby

47

The Darkness

I was running, faster and faster. Darkness was coming, I could feel it, even smell it. Swinging round, my foot went flying. I hit my target, but the force when it connected pushed me over. The metal was driven through my heart. Everything went black, black, black.

Kate Wallis (12)
Brooke Weston City Technology College, Corby

Heaven's Not Enough

Heaven's not enough. It's empty and cold. Everyone pretends to be happy, when their hearts are trapped in sorrow. Their souls have gone and nobody remembers them. You float forever with nothing but eyes to watch the happy, free ones below; it's an endless sleep. Here, I don't remember you.

Laura Keeble (14)
Brooke Weston City Technology College, Corby

Turbulence

I approach the toilet … turn the handle. It's locked.
'I'm in here,' a voice exclaims. I wait, 2, 3, 4, 5
minutes, watching, waiting. Someone else edges
towards me. Turbulence shakes the plane. They stare
at the handle, 'No one's in there!' they say!

Amy Smith (14)
Brooke Weston City Technology College, Corby

Redemption Of Humanity

Tick-tock, clock ticking. *Tick-tock*, gun raised. *Tick-tock*, Earth's time nearly up. Artemis manoeuvred the plane away from civilisation. *Tick-tock*, time nearly up. Opal fired, but Artemis avoided the shot and fell from the aircraft. *Tick-tock*, parachute opened – *tick-tock*, world was safe. They knew nothing …

Peter Hutchinson (14)
Brooke Weston City Technology College, Corby

51

School Playground

One minute left until half-time, a foul occured, the ref held a red card in the air. A fight started, punching and headlocks. Yet the game still continued. The ball went flying through the air. Centre back Tom got hit right in the face. Laughter filled the air.

Beth Malloy (14)

Brooke Weston City Technology College, Corby

Someone Else's Work Of Art

Flawless to the eye. Daunting, daring her. Never to
be good enough. She's shaking, stirring, seething.
All for show, shut out from reality. A role model,
superstar, even heroine.
'Why?' she asks. Haunted by past mistakes, emotion
overwhelming. The force to be known, desired.
Taken in by image, popularity, insecurities.

Lauren Albrecht (14)
Brooke Weston City Technology College, Corby

Crispy Duck

I'm the only one left. After the craze for crispy duck started, all my friends were the first in line for the honour of becoming crispy duck. How amazing would it be; so crunchy yet so adorably soft. You could eat me with anything! I wish I were a duck.

Rachael Coffins (14)
Brooke Weston City Technology College, Corby

54

Gun Crime - Tick Time

Tick. Tick. Tick.
This noise is completely incessant.
Tick. Tick. Tick.
The cogs in my head are constantly turning, grinding.
Tick. Tick. Tick.
Blood rushing from my chest like a crimson river.
Tick. Tick. Tick.
My focus concentrated onto one thing.
Tick. Tick. Tick.
And, finally the word comes …
Dead.

Deromi Jessiman (14)
Brooke Weston City Technology College, Corby

Untitled

The boy ran for his life through the forest of the damned being chased by the ghost of Istania. He had woken the spirits from their rest as he searched for the golden sword of light. As many others he failed his journey, searching for the sword.
He was killed.

Chris McGhee (14)

Brooke Weston City Technology College, Corby

Agnes Meredith's Mystery

Standing in darkness with only a flashlight for
guidance. Cold sweat raises the hairs on my neck as
a rat scurries past me into the indefinite gloom of
ebony. I stood embarking cluelessly on the murder
of Agnes, concentrating on any irregularities of the
chilling murder scene …
'I've got it!'

Brendan Farrell (13)
Brooke Weston City Technology College, Corby

Untitled

Why does it rain, it rains so hard. Floods, floods and more floods. The water rushes in. Everything is destroyed, floors, kitchens, couches, TVs, gone, gone, gone. People run home running for their lives. Water swallowing people up. They are all gone. Wind howls. Bye bye.

Alex Barrowman (14)
Brooke Weston City Technology College, Corby

Untitled

My world was closing in. I knew that my world was ending. I clenched my mum and dad's hands, knowing I was going to die. I couldn't hold on any longer. I opened my eyes, looked up. My hands weakened. I knew this was it. I looked up, I'd gone.

Kessey Ingram (14)
Brooke Weston City Technology College, Corby

Me And Him = Never

As I stared across the maths room, he smiled. I panicked, looked at my work and thought how my legs turn to jelly and my heart melts! He came over smiling. My heart racing!
'Can I borrow a pen?'
My heart stopped! Disappointed! Does he even notice? I love you!

Sasha Wakelin (14)
Brooke Weston City Technology College, Corby

My Grinding Dream

The silver grinding against the saw was deafening. I sprinted far away, the grinding was heard against the birds. Their sound made me realise my lost dream. I ran through the forest only leaving the monkeys behind, finally I found my dream. I swore I would never let it crumble!

Ryan McGreavey (12)
Brooke Weston City Technology College, Corby

61

War Mum

It was overwhelming. The sadness of losing my mum engulfed me. It was the day of the funeral and a strange silence was present in the crowd. My mum was there, her old war friends. They were in the Iraq war. She was brutally ambushed.

George Cotteff (12)
Brooke Weston City Technology College, Corby

Wanderer

'The girl was discarded in the back streets of Brooklyn, abandoned by mankind with only her invisible guardian to protect her …'
Erin's life never began, she came from nowhere, lives nowhere and is no one, I am the only one who can share her story of terror where she met the Wanderer.

Emily Rayner
Brooke Weston City Technology College, Corby

Fate!

Alone in a place which wasn't my own. Scared of knowing the truth. Footsteps ... my heart was thumping out of my chest. Thoughts racing through my head. One thought led to another. The door creaked open, slowly like it was playing with my mind. Vulnerable? Revenged? My fate had arrived!

Emily Lynch
Brooke Weston City Technology College, Corby

Haunted House

An old house was covered in the freezing winter's snow. An old man drinking his warm cup of coffee, nice and relaxed, apart from the fact there was someone else in his house, someone he didn't know about, maybe his murderer.

Jake Stevenson
Brooke Weston City Technology College, Corby

In The Navy

We were sitting below deck, playing cards. When we were put on red alert. We were being attacked from above. Men were on deck getting in position to save our boat. We had men on the air missile guns, we also had men with handguns. We were prepared for attack.

Chris Guiver
Brooke Weston City Technology College, Corby

The Ghostly Light

The whistling wind of death crept upon the cottage that had once been filled with laughter, lay awake shivering to the sound of the broken piano thudding empty notes, searching high and low, a shocking surprise awaited me in the oak tree, in a ghostly light my nearly dead grandad.

Leigh Brown
Brooke Weston City Technology College, Corby

Best Friends

It was another school day. Lauren and Anya were at school. One day their teacher said, 'Lauren it is your Keith Grammar induction days in a week.'
On Tuesday Lauren went to Keith Grammar. Then Anya and the rest of the class went to Buckie. Even now they're still friends.

Karen Burgess (12)
Buckie High School, Buckie

Dogs Afloat

One day two dogs called Scott and Ron were going on an adventure in a boat. They passed a rock nearby and saw a golden ball but it wasn't a bone. Scott and Ron just took a glimpse and found a golden bone. Scott and Ron were very, very happy.

Ryan Munro (11)
Buckie High School, Buckie

The Fall Out

'Meet you at the park,' Jodi shouted.
'OK,' replied Holly.
Holly arrived at the park and Jodi wasn't there!
At school they had an argument and made faces at each other!
Later that night they made friends and went out. Jodi said she was sorry. They were best friends again!

Kiara Anderson (11)
Buckie High School, Buckie

Untitled

Buckie was going to the final.
The final was the next day. It was Keith's kick off.
James got it easily and hit it first time. Goal!
In the second half Keith scored two goals. Kris had
the ball, he took a shot but James was in the way.

Macauly Flaws (12)
Buckie High School, Buckie

71

Enemies

The two girls were having great fun with each other. The two girls walked to the park and played. Then another girl came along and she took her friend away. After a couple of days Kirsten came to her and said that she doesn't want to be her friend anymore.

Kirstie Redford
Buckie High School, Buckie

Lost In The Forest

Bob and Jim decided to go to the forest. In the forest they decided to make a hut. They had a fight about where to put it. It was getting dark. They couldn't find their way out. They had to work together to get out and they were friends again.

Keiran Riddoch (11)
Buckie High School, Buckie

The Ultimatum

He runs out into the dusty road, her long hair trails behind her as she runs ahead.
'Wait!' he calls, but his desperate attempts to be heard are in vain. She does not hear. The rain starts to fall as he realises he will never see his daughter again.

Emma Rogers (17)
Burgess Hill School, Burgess Hill

One-Legged Ella

Cinderella was late for a party so she phoned her
friend for a lift in her helicopter. Because it was dark
they landed in a field. She climbed an electric fence
and lost her leg.
The next day people were taking her leg around the
doors waiting for a claim.

Leanne Cannon (13)
Craigroyston Community High School, Edinburgh

The Electric Chair

Looking face to face at myself, water flowing is what
I hear. Cold bristles make overflowing pain, forcing
it to be pulled away. Tastes like a battery, which
is blood ejecting. It sprays over the cylinder bowl
shape. The words which follow 'I hate my teeth'.

Craig Stevenson (13)
Craigroyston Community High School, Edinburgh

Kids In America

It was September 2002. It happened in America. I
was with my mum and dad. I could see fireworks
and kids dancing. I could hear the loud fireworks and
people singing. I was standing watching the show. I
felt excited, happy. It ended when we went back to
the hotel.

Jodie Harkins (14)
Craigroyston Community High School, Edinburgh

Glenntress

2 weeks ago I went to Glenntress with Ian and Sean with a club. I felt excited. It is a bike place where lots of people go. I can remember hearing birds. I only hurt myself 3 times on the whole trip. I really enjoyed it. It was great.

Tommy Macdonald (13)
Craigroyston Community High School, Edinburgh

Cinderzilla And His Golden Zimmer Frame

Cinderzilla is in his house, playing his PS2. When a gold zimmer frame appears and grants him a wish, he wishes to be young again. It happens and a girl comes to his house. They get married, die of fright in the morning and leave everything to their pet dog.

Dean Jones (13)

Craigroyston Community High School, Edinburgh

Niece's Birthday

Monday, my niece's birthday. At 2am I got a call on my mobile telling me to send a card. I just won the lottery with my ticket and I was on an island. I took my wooden spoon, Sellotape, card and rubber duck and used them to send the card.

Keith Marshall (14)
Craigroyston Community High School, Edinburgh

Turkey '06

I went to Turkey in 2006 on holiday. We were sitting by the pool and my cousin Lewis jumped into the big pool and nearly drowned. My dad jumped in and got him out. He was only in shock and fine. He was a very brave two year old.

Ashley Osborne (13)
Craigroyston Community High School, Edinburgh

Cinderelly From The Hood

Cinderelly is from the hood, she lives with her dad and obese two sisters. She meets an ogre who she lives with then they divorce. She meets a homeless man who turns out to be the love of her life, has 48 kids and lives happily ever after.

Laura Cunningham (13)
Craigroyston Community High School, Edinburgh

Best Birthday Ever!

It was my birthday. I got a mobile phone and a lottery ticket in my card, it was a winner. I won 10.5 million. I bought a wooden spoon factory and started selling Sellotape. Then my mum bought me a rubber duck. I have no idea why.

Thomas Graham (13)
Craigroyston Community High School, Edinburgh

83

My Dream

I was scared. He was running as fast as he could and he was right behind me. The big bully was after me for no reason. He caught me and I didn't know what he was going to do to me. He threw me on the floor. I woke up.

Jack Heppleston (12)
Flint High School, Flint

Let Life Be So It Won't Hurt You

My life was normal. I had owned a big cat. She was on the streets – she had escaped. She was a good cat. But instinct took over when I found her. She was too hungry to think. I was left there with her, as cold as ice.

Bethan Phillips (13)
Flint High School, Flint

85

Too Fast To Think

The wind in my face, I was being thrown about,
it was too fast to think about. I felt my head was
pounding with adrenalin. I could feel my head being
thrashed about then it all went silent. I was stopping.
I was happy.
I survived Rita Queen of speed.

Jessica Parry (12)
Flint High School, Flint

The Vampire

The eyes were dark. The blood shone on his teeth.
The son of the Devil came closer and closer. This
was not how I imagined death. He struck me hard.
His strength was unimaginable. Blood dripped from
my nose. Soon I would lose a lot more.
I screamed.
He laughed.

Charlotte Owen (12)
Flint High School, Flint

87

Vengeance Isn't Sweet

Strike!
The corpse of my wife. Her violet lips radiate her
innocence. Wait! The culprit must receive vengeance.
What would Maggie have wanted? I know I shouldn't
have hit her. It's too late. Isn't it enough punishment
to know I've taken my wife's soul? No. I thought not.

Rochelle Bedford (13)
Flint High School, Flint

The Chase

The man was speeding down the road with the police after him. He did a runner into the trees by the road. The police followed him. There they were on the cliff with the sea raging behind them. The man tumbled and fell into the raging current below and died.

James Roberts (12)
Flint High School, Flint

The Night Of Torture

A little girl was sitting in the corner with tears rolling down her bruised eye. Trying to blank out the screaming coming from upstairs, then the sound of footsteps racing down the stairs, and the door banging. As it shut the girl began to get out while she could.

Hannah Brown (13)
Flint High School, Flint

The Car Crash

They rushed him down the corridor as quick as their legs could carry them right into recess and the doctor was trying to make him calm. They checked him over and found out he had broke his leg in three places and had a dislocated shoulder and needed an operation.

Shaun Jones (15)
Flint High School, Flint

Dead End

A man in a shop was loitering.
He sneaked a packet of cigarettes in his pocket but
the shopkeeper saw him. He ran. The shopkeeper
gave chase. I rang the police. He had been captured.
He was arrested for theft and rape. He was jailed for
six years.

James Ruby Peart (14)
Flint High School, Flint

The Hand

Every night I lie in bed just waiting for it to come again. It hits 12.30 and there it is. I sit up, my adrenaline is rushing. It grabs me, so frozen in fear I can't scream. It pulls me under the bed. I was never seen again.

Tayla Handforth (13)
Flint High School, Flint

93

Ghost

I was there alone, I heard that noise again and again. *What was it?* I wondered. I checked. It was a ghost. I screamed, I ran for my life. It followed and killed me.

Jake Massey (13)
Flint High School, Flint

The Seagull

Down at the pier, swimming, we ended up on a small island. Hundreds of them flew over us. We tried. 'Nearly back!' I shouted. I grabbed the ladder. Turned back. He was caught in seaweed. I swam back. The seaweed was tight around his legs. Then a seagull swooped down …

Shannon Campbell (12)
Glenlola Collegiate School, Bangor

My Holiday

On holiday I went. I met him, my Prince Charming.
Love at first sight. We laughed and loved, that's all.
But! Soon we left, departed at the airport. I thought,
oh no what can we do? We kissed and left and said
goodbye. I cried and cried until I died.

Holly Auld (12)

Glenlola Collegiate School, Bangor

The Day Animals Turned On Humans

I wouldn't go to the zoo today, the park, the forest, the animal shelter or even your own home! The animals have turned on humans, even the fluffy little hamsters! The fish chomped at fishermen, dogs attacked owners and cats clawed at little girls! Uh-oh … here comes Buster.

Harriet Gillespie (12)
Glenlola Collegiate School, Bangor

Walking In The Woods

I walk to my granny's through the woods. I hear people laughing, howling, barking, *snap!* What's that? It's OK, I've just stepped on a branch. Rain spitting. It's too dark to see the trees. I suddenly hear someone coming towards me. I see green eyes! I scream. I run away.

Jessica Berry (12)
Glenlola Collegiate School, Bangor

Scared

I'm running, the heat's unbearable and my eyes are straining to stay open. I have no control over which way I'm going. It feels like I'm being smacked by the wind. I'm constantly being thrown back. Then I hit a wall. I can't feel the ground. Next thing, I'm awake.

Hannah Gibson (12)
Glenlola Collegiate School, Bangor

It Was Just A Dream

I walked in the front door. I sat down to watch the television. The lounge door closed. There's only me. Alone. In the house. 'Who's there? Is it you Mum?' I shouted but there was no reply. Just silence. I heard a creak. Someone grabbed me! I woke up sweating.

Rebecca Davison (12)
Glenlola Collegiate School, Bangor

100

The Day I Nearly Died

I felt myself slowly floating downwards. In the distance I heard my dad's voice calling out to me. I tried to get air but instead I gulped in a mouthful of water. Suddenly I felt someone grab my arm and I was dragged to the surface.

Ashleigh Fulton (12)

Glenlola Collegiate School, Bangor

The Eyes

Midnight – the grand clock sounded. I went to get a drink. Windows lying open, floorboards creaking, lights flickering. Lights off. My heart pounded. The door creaked. I felt a tap on my shoulder. Heavy breathing. I stop breathing. I stumble, I fall. I see shiny, green, angry glaring eyes.
Darkness.

Sarah Baifie (12)
Glenlola Collegiate School, Bangor

Cliffhanger

We are running, chasing, playing. Bounding through fields of daisies. Sun shining brightly. Having so much fun. Suddenly, the wind picks up. She is gone. I skid to a halt. I see her, dangling from a cliff. Her fingers are clinging on. I see her falling. She screams. I jump.

Louise Black (12)

Glenlola Collegiate School, Bangor

The Sleepwalker

'Right,' said Mum, 'try not to sleepwalk.'
'I'll try.' I fall into a deep deep sleep. I dream about
roller coasters and theme parks. Then suddenly I'm
jerked awake. I find myself digging my feet into the
chair in front, the wind beating into my face. And I
shoot downwards.

Hoffi Burgon (12)
Glenlola Collegiate School, Bangor

My Dog Storm

My puppy Storm is black and white. She nibbles anything and everything. She tries to lick everyone and she always jumps up on people but can be scared of strangers. I think she is so cute because wherever you sit she will come and curl up beside you!

Trana-Rebecca Gray (12)
Glenlola Collegiate School, Bangor

105

Shipwrecked

I'm at sea. Sailing. It's a beautiful hot day. I have been out for hours.

The sky darkened. It began raining. Heavier and heavier. I felt it hit my head, by now the waves were huge. The boat overturned. Next thing I know, I'm on a desert island. Shipwrecked.

Kerry Baird (12)
Glenlola Collegiate School, Bangor

Darkness

I wake up. It's late. I sit up and quietly yawn. I look around. Darkness. I get out of bed. I go to turn on my light. Nothing. I go to my family's bedrooms. No one is there. I creep downstairs, petrified, wanting normality. Someone taps me. Fearful. Frozen. Unfamiliar.

Rachel Bolton (12)
Glenlola Collegiate School, Bangor

107

Running

I ran and ran, until my feet couldn't take it any more.
I could feel my heart in my throat as I went faster and
faster. My head was pounding, my feet aching. I was
nearly there! But I was too tired, I pressed stop and
got off the treadmill.

Jessica Broom (12)
Heolddu Comprehensive School, Bargoed

The Dreamer

I was taken by surprise when I saw it. The most horrid thing I had ever seen! But what was it? I couldn't tell. Just as I moved towards it I recognised what it was. But a beam of light came from its heart. Then I realised I was dreaming.

Danielle Meffy (12)
Heolddu Comprehensive School, Bargoed

My Cat

I was lying in bed awake, listening to Tabby my cat trying to get in. What was she doing out? I took myself downstairs to let her in. There it was, the back door. I opened it. I stared. There was something there. But it was not my little Tabby.

Abigail Edwards (12)
Heolddu Comprehensive School, Bargoed

The Swimming Gala

I took a deep breath and dived under. 'Go on Sarah, you can do it!' Splashing, kicking I was nearly there. My goggles filled with water, chlorine splashing into my mouth. I could see my opponent. I pushed my hand to the wall. A big cheer echoed, I had won!

Olivia Jones (12)
Heolddu Comprehensive School, Bargoed

The Swamp

The night gathered itself up and unleashed its grip of the night sky. It revealed a swamp, green and slimy. Little green frogs jumped out of the water and started swimming in and out of each other, splashing, diving. Suddenly, a French hunter came sneakily and killed all the frogs.

Stuart Davies (12)
Heolddu Comprehensive School, Bargoed

Bullying Betty

Betty, in school, bullies my friend. We took revenge, taping ghostly noises and tying strings to library books. Later we hid in the closet. Betty came, tape turned on. Betty turned round, pulled the strings and books went flying into her face! With a yell, she ran. No more bullying.

Rachael Pippen (12)
Heolddu Comprehensive School, Bargoed

113

The Present

'Wow! What a present, who's it off?' I asked.
'I don't know,' Mum replied.
I opened it, a sharp light glaring into my eyes.
Suddenly a strange feeling coursed through my
body then I appeared in another place or world
underground, a ghostly forest. The present was a
vortex!

William Dunford (13)
Heolddu Comprehensive School, Bargoed

114

The Newquay Miracle

'Anyone sitting here? No, OK then.' I sat down alone.
It's a lovely view from up here. I'd never been on a
roofless double-decker. Around the sea front we go!
Oh, you can see dolphins, dancing and undulating in
the waves. A Newquay miracle!

Kirsty Reynolds (12)
Heolddu Comprehensive School, Bargoed

The UFO

The girl walked through the gate and screamed.
There was a flash of green light. Then the wind blew
really hard and almost blew the girl right off the
ground. She saw flashing lights in the sky and also
a UFO floating. She started to float. She had been
abducted.

Rebecca Ingram-Jones (13)
Heolddu Comprehensive School, Bargoed

Late

Ryan ran from his house onto the street. He darted along, certain that he would be late for the match. Unable to get in, he searched for an entrance, which he found. In the corridor, Ryan made for an opening, then froze. He was in the middle of the pitch.

Darren Bookless (13)

Heolddu Comprehensive School, Bargoed

The Night I Found You!

I was sitting quietly alone. I heard a faint whisper, frantically I turned. No one was there. I turned and sat down again. Putting my feet up I began to relax. The sound came again. I looked down under the stool and there looking up at me was a cat.

Carol Smith (14)
Heolddu Comprehensive School, Bargoed

The Monster

One stormy night in the forest a big green slobbery monster popped out of the trees, dripping blood out of his sharp black teeth. He tried to speak but I ran away. He tried to catch me. It was nearly dawn. I thought, *if I keep running he will go.*

Jessica Morgan Chipperfield (12)
Heolddu Comprehensive School, Bargoed

Never Should Have Let Go

I never should have let go of his hand in the crowd. I went and partied with these guys I didn't even know, tonight I will sleep by myself and I will never lose the guilt. I will lie awake worrying myself sick. I never should have let go.

Chloe Davies (12)
Heolddu Comprehensive School, Bargoed

Forgotten

I forgot him at the train station. I should never have gone into the cafe but the pastries looked so nice and oh those charming blue eyes. He was no longer there when I finally remembered for a pair of blue eyes and an apricot strudel. Tonight, I sleep alone.

Annalisse Roberts (13)
Heolddu Comprehensive School, Bargoed

A Dark Night In The Forest

It was dark and no one was around, just me. I was walking home from my friend's house and I heard a noise then something gripped me up and dragged me somewhere. I screamed and someone said, 'It's OK.' It was all dark and I was scared.

Harley Duggan (12)
Heolddu Comprehensive School, Bargoed

Night In A Forest

It was a dark night and I was walking home through a forest. I could hear footsteps behind me. I turned around quickly. Then suddenly something hit me hard on my head. I felt cold and dead. It wasn't till I woke up and realised it was just a dream.

Alysha Davies (12)
Heolddu Comprehensive School, Bargoed

The Moonlight

The moonlight shone upon the dark blue sea, leaving a bright and white circle dancing in the dark. I stood alone on cold dirty sand letting my thoughts dive through the air. With a shudder I turned back and disappeared as the wind howled through the cold, horrible, dark night.

Ashleigh Jones (12)
Heolddu Comprehensive School, Bargoed

The Figure

I was terrified more than I had ever been before in my life. I thought I was in a dream but I was more awake than ever. I was running through a corridor and then I tripped. That was a surprise. Suddenly I looked behind me and it got me.

Daniel Jones (12)
Heolddu Comprehensive School, Bargoed

Too Cool For School

The sun shone bright as Jack started walking through the park on his way to school Suddenly some boys came running at him and started pushing him. They told him not to go to school. They said he was too cool for school. He was caught that day.

Jack Chard (12)
Heolddu Comprehensive School, Bargoed

Hallowe'en Night

Hallowe'en night, we were in a house party dressed up, my heart was pounding to the bass of the banging music. I met a girl in a demon costume. We went outside and I said, 'Take off your mask.'
She replied, 'I'm not wearing a mask,' and instantly killed me.

Grant Sullivan (12)
Heolddu Comprehensive School, Bargoed

Too Cool For School

I walked down the path. I crossed the road and found myself standing in front of my boring school, rain splashing, sounds of thunder closing my eardrums to the max and wearing my uniform.
I stood in front of the school and said, 'I'm too cool for every school.'

Jamie Cobley (12)
Heolddu Comprehensive School, Bargoed

The Journey

I took an amazing journey to America, it was
fantastic, all the lights and cameras. I saw myself on
stage in front of millions of people.
'I'm famous,' I said to myself.
I heard my mother calling me, 'Get up love.'
After all, it was only a dream.

Luke Effaway & Thomas Carter (12)
Heolddu Comprehensive School, Bargoed

The Baby Seal

One snowy day a baby seal was lying down
daydreaming. He had welcoming black eyes and a
white furry coat. Snowflakes fell softly to the ground.
He could see his mother in the far distance. A
shadow came darkly over him. *Bang!*
The innocent baby seal was tortured to death.

Emma Carter
Heolddu Comprehensive School, Bargoed

Love?

He walked away and left her to cry. Those two
words and she wanted to die. She thought it was love
but she was wrong. Now she's lying at the bottom of
the lake all because he walked away. So if this is love,
well, I think I will wait.

Lacey Price (13)

Heolddu Comprehensive School, Bargoed

131

Alice In Wonderland

Alice ran into the field, looking left and right. She tumbled into the Queen of Hearts who turned and screamed, 'Off with her head!'
An axeman hurried forward obsequiously axe raised, slipped and cut the Queen's foot. Oh horror!
'That hurt! Off with his head!'
'But I chopped them off!'

Bethan Jenkins (14)
Heolddu Comprehensive School, Bargoed

Tim The Clown

'Ow!' Tim yelled as he strolled into a closing door of a train while looking down at his big shoes. Tim was a suicidal clown. He then realised that his shoes were trapped in the door when the train started to move. Everyone started laughing. He was finally very funny.

Ben Heatley (14)
Heolddu Comprehensive School, Bargoed

The Rock Show

At the gig the band went wild: eight thousand people swaying whilst singing every word back to their favourite band as if the lyrics are their own. The lead singer points. A fan joins him on stage, singing with their hero, feeling like one of the band. A star.

Menna Bradford (14)
Heolddu Comprehensive School, Bargoed

Dragon

Dragon in the forest, torching what he liked. People
were afraid of the blaze so very bright. But then
stepped forth a hero, clothed in the green of fields.
He wielded a mighty sword and legendary shield.
He looked invincible, unafraid of death. But he
underestimated the dragon's mighty breath.

Jordan Forbes (14)
Heolddu Comprehensive School, Bargoed

The Three Little Pigs

There were three little pigs. They built houses. They were made out of straw, wood and bricks. A wolf came along. He blew the straw and wood house down. The two pigs moved into their brother's house. The wolf couldn't blow the brick house down. After blowing hard he exploded.

Gary Pine (14)
Heolddu Comprehensive School, Bargoed

Untitled

The teacher yelled, 'Be quiet for once.'
I shouted twice as loud. 'I'm too cool to be quiet.'
She sent me to the headmaster. I was suspended
for two weeks. I came back, did it the same. I never
learned. I got expelled.
I wish I had learnt right now.

Chantelle Davies (14)
Heolddu Comprehensive School, Bargoed

A Misunderstanding

'We're under attack!' cried Commander Octavian.
'The alien scum, attack! Repel them!'
But it was hopeless, the unknown invaders had
vaulted the wall, their leader had fought his way to
the commander, leaving destruction in his wake. He
asked in a booming voice, 'Can I have my ball back
please?'

Jack Thompson (14)
Heolddu Comprehensive School, Bargoed

Untitled

I ran across the desert chasing a pink and yellow spotty lizard when suddenly the lizard turned around and gave an evil smile, it was looking very hungry. I found myself running away from it. I ran through the oasis of peace when it caught me and ate me alive.

Natasha Muffer (14)
Heolddu Comprehensive School, Bargoed

Down The Dark Road

As I was walking down the pitch-black road there was a bright light that shone across the edge of the road. I went to investigate but as I got closer the light went dimmer. I thought to myself, *what is wrong?* But then it went completely out …

Anton Mizen (13)
John Masefield High School, Ledbury

The Competition

I was at the drop in ramp, my heart beating fast as lightning. The crowd cheering me on as I dropped in. Suddenly, I hit the ramp doing a 360° backflip, it felt like I'd been sucked into a twister. The relief when I hit the floor. I did it!

Peter Foster (14)
John Masefield High School, Ledbury

141

Mystery In The House

One day two boys Tom and Jim went up an
overgrown drive. They saw an old battered house,
they heard a scream.
'What was that?' Jim asked.
'Don't know!'
They went in the door… a scream!
'What was that? Tom, Tom! Where are you? Stop
messing around Tom …'

George Banner (13)
John Masefield High School, Ledbury

Run

I ran as fast as I could. Wind whooshing past my face,
I stopped, looked behind, glared at the mist to see
if I could spot any blurry faces getting near. They
shouted, I ran so fast it felt as if I was flying, will I get
away? I was scared.

Parisa Saberi (13)
John Masefield High School, Ledbury

143

What Was That?

It was a dark and stormy night. The wind swept through the trees. Jessie was walking through the woods trying to get home. She stopped dead. What was that sound? A rustling of leaves then out came a badger! Jessie screamed! She woke up; it was only a scary dream.

Becky Brown (13)
John Masefield High School, Ledbury

Sniper

I sprinted down the darkened alleyway. Enveloped
in the shadows I slammed into the damaged wall
stealthily shuffling across. I climbed the rusted ladder
and launched myself onto the rooftops. I lay down,
pulling out my rifle, placing it into my hands, adjusting
my metallic scope, tension building up inside …

Connor Bufton (14)
John Masefield High School, Ledbury

145

Waterlogged

As we boarded the plane I remembered the shining blue waves crashing down on my house sweeping all my belongings out. But wait, I searched my pocket, it wasn't there. I ran away from the plane. My gran stopped me. That was it; I had lost my most important possession.

Katy Layton (14)
John Masefield High School, Ledbury

Get Revenge

There was heavy fire to my right; I shot back, missing by inches. I dived out and hit right in the middle of the pole head. I carried on walking through the abandoned city, only six towns to go before I find what I'm looking for, my brave father's killer.

Jack Vernaff (14)
John Masefield High School, Ledbury

147

Bright Lights

The bright light was blinding my eyes. As a door opened, smoke appeared and I tried to get away. A tall shadow crept towards me and I froze. The bright lights faded and I couldn't now see its face. Then it happened … the fist words of inhuman life were spoken!

Hannah Bowring (14)
John Masefield High School, Ledbury

148

Journey To My Destination

As we set out on our journey to the Arctic, we had packed all our fluffy coats and clothes. We had travelled with vengeance and kept moving. As we spotted our destination on the horizon, our hearts filled with joy, we had done it, I had done it again!

Alice Perrett (14)
John Masefield High School, Ledbury

149

The Game

I ran. I was running as fast as I could. I could hear
footsteps behind me. I looked behind me; they were
on my left and right. I kept running, dodging through
the people. Up the stairs round the corner, I turned
again then, 'Tag!'
I was *it*, damn!

Effen Jones (14)
John Masefield High School, Ledbury

I'm Spinning Around

There I was, my head was spinning, I had a funny feeling in my stomach. I was sure I was going to throw up. I closed my eyes tight, I didn't want to look. The cold breeze gave me a shiver down my spine, I really do hate the twister.

Kayleigh Pugh (14)
John Masefield High School, Ledbury

151

Frozen

My heart was in my mouth as the beast was coming closer. Tears were running down my face. We reached the top and fell down a massive drop. We were getting so fast my ears nearly popped with the wind against my face. I was frozen, I could not move!

Ben Adams (14)
John Masefield High School, Ledbury

The Dream

I was running through the huge candyfloss like clouds.
I was scared; I didn't know what was happening. Was
this real or a dream? I started running, faster and
faster, it kept chasing me. I woke up, it was a dream,
a bird had been chasing me the whole time!

Emily Ffeck (14)
John Masefield High School, Ledbury

The Lost Power

It was only a few moments ago Max found that he had immense powers, stronger than anyone known in the universe. He suddenly got an overpowering rage. His eyes flared up into a fiery light, his hands reached out and flames surged across, massacring a poor defenceless old man.

Scott Lincoln (14)
John Masefield High School, Ledbury

154

The Assassin

He gripped the sniper, slowly bringing it up and putting it into his cold hands leaning it against the window while taking aim. His scared eye was fixed on the target. His finger slid into position … *bang!* She was dead, killed by the cold-hearted assassin ready to kill again.

Tom Parsons (14)
John Masefield High School, Ledbury

What Could It Be?

It was the end of the summer holidays. Robert had been staying in his grandparents' cabin in the forest. At night he heard howls and things rustle outside. He looked outside and saw eyes stare back. What could it be? Will he find out more when he returns next summer?

Naomi Parry (14)
John Masefield High School, Ledbury

My Life

I thought it was a dream but it wasn't that day I was taken away from Mum. She is the other half of a heart that completes me. I would love to be with her right now but unfortunately I can't. I love her with all my heart, please, please!

Sarah Brown (14)
John Masefield High School, Ledbury

157

The Lonely Orange

Once upon a fruit bowl, there lived an orange. He was very lonely because he had only one friend. That friend was the bowl, Fred. Fred didn't talk much, he just made funny knocking noises when Orange jumped up and down. Sadly, Orange lived a long life with no friends.

Offy Davies-Hodges (14)
John Masefield High School, Ledbury

The Story Of John Box

There was a young boy called John walking down a small, dark, dirty alleyway. About halfway down he saw an old homeless man. The man was stumbling, John kept on walking. He was scared. John struggled as the man hit him, he ducked under his arm and then ran away.

Tony Foster (14)
John Masefield High School, Ledbury

Coming

Jack's foot splashed the puddles as he sprinted home.
They were coming for him, nobody else. If they got
him, the unthinkable would happen. If they got him
Jack would never be the same again. He stopped,
they were there! Jack's aunties bent down and kissed
Jack's whimpering face.

Elizabeth Williams (14)
John Masefield High School, Ledbury

160

The Spy

As I stepped into the school gates, I knew what I had to do. Like every school day instead of going to registration I go to the staffroom. I pressed across left five times until a gap in the floor appeared, why was I still a spy?

Seana Russell (13)
John Masefield High School, Ledbury

Alive Or Dead?

I was so nervous as the plane suddenly shook in the sky. The plane weaved from side to side cutting through the air. Shaking and plunging down. We were heading for the ocean but there was a sudden dip and we landed, crashing into the rocks … to be continued!

Brittany Dance (13)
John Masefield High School, Ledbury

Untitled

I wasn't sure where I was going, I was up then I was down. When I was awake I was surrounded by people, in maths I was laughed at, they had swords in their hands. I was tied up nowhere to go like a fat pig in a pen.

Jed Yaxley (13)
John Masefield High School, Ledbury

The Stalker

Dark as dark, black as black, nothing in sight, not a noise, the feeling that someone was watching me stalked me as I was running around in circles trying to calm down. I felt someone grab me and put a bag over my head.

Adam Paske (12)
John Masefield High School, Ledbury

Worst Nightmare

Rocking backwards and forwards staring at the clock, waiting for time to pass. *Tick-tock, tick-tock.* The clock chimed 1pm; she heard a horrendous scream coming from upstairs. She clenched her fist, she curled up in a ball waiting for someone to come and get her but nobody came.

Charlotte Firth (12)
John Masefield High School, Ledbury

The Little Dinosaur

Tim was a small dinosaur. One day Tim wanted to go for a walk because the other dinosaurs were teasing him because he was small and weak. But he said, 'I'm going to get bigger and stronger then you.' But all the other dinosaurs were laughing at him.

Kane Weir (13)
John Masefield High School, Ledbury

166

Untitled

In the dead of night I was asleep until I heard a noise from downstairs. I went to investigate. I started to get freaked out; I couldn't see where the noise came from. I went back upstairs wary of what the noise could have been.
I couldn't sleep.

Kieran Phillips (13)
John Masefield High School, Ledbury

The Puppy

Once there was a boy called Fred. He lived in a flat.
He was earning money to buy a pet because Fred
had no friends. He earned enough money to buy a
puppy.
One day he went to work and came home to find his
house was all torn up.

Mike Green (13)
John Masefield High School, Ledbury

Untitled

One day I was walking down a little alleyway on my way to work. It was pitch-black. As I got further down the alley, there was a bridge. I got closer to the bridge, it got colder. Eventually I got to the bridge, I was shivering, I ran.

Steven Rawle (12)
John Masefield High School, Ledbury

The End

As I ran up the steep hill I could see my misty breath in the icy air. I saw him floating silently up the hill. I ran until ... dead end ... a vertical cliff! I looked back; he was getting closer and closer, I jumped ... I fell and fell and *smack!*

Alice Leaper (12)

John Masefield High School, Ledbury

The Day We Went Out

A car broke down on the side of the road, there were two girls in it. A man said, 'Come with me.' One girl got tied up, one shrieked and she was dead. The other girl ran and then *bang*, she was dead and the man is still out there.

Gemma Impey (13)
John Masefield High School, Ledbury

171

Untitled

I went on holiday to Hastings and we went on a day trip to a place called Smugglers' Adventure. Smugglers' Adventure was a very big cave where the smugglers kept all their gold. They made up a ghost story so that people didn't go in caves to steal.

Terry Smith (13)
John Masefield High School, Ledbury

172

The One House With One Man

One day these two boys Leon and Bob went into a house far away. No one goes there, no one comes out. But one night Leon and Bob saw a man go in the house. They followed him in and the door shut, would they ever come out?

Kamal Morgan (13)
John Masefield High School, Ledbury

A View Through A Rifle

The view through this rifle wasn't rabbit or a hare
but a man aimed right at his head. This wasn't real of
course or was it? The sound that you hear next isn't
a pleasing one – the sound of the rifle being loaded
with a bullet. Quiet then … *bang!*

Daniel Garside (14)
John Masefield High School, Ledbury

On Edge . . .

He held his old wrinkled hand out towards her; she nervously went to shake it. He gripped her cold, tiny fingers. His huge body loomed over her as he came closer he whispered in her ear, 'Help me!' Then suddenly fell to the ground, dead!

Leanne Vina (14)
John Masefield High School, Ledbury

Untitled

'Thief, I'll kill you!' Hannah froze. Her heart was in her mouth. The crazy man charged towards her and reached for something. A knife! Suddenly Hannah ran. She dropped the small item screaming but the thudding stopped. Hannah looked back, he was gone. Hannah collapsed stunned.

Tiffany Ryder (14)
John Masefield High School, Ledbury

Trousers

While walking to the shop he realised that something was wrong. When he got there the shopkeeper said, 'Haven't you forgotten something?' He looked down and saw he'd forgotten his trousers he felt so embarrassed! Everyone started laughing, he ran home crying. When he got home he was still embarrassed.

Ashley Gillespie (14)
John Masefield High School, Ledbury

The Bus Driver

While I was walking to school I heard something in the bush, it was a man with a knife! I screamed my head off. I ran to the bus stop and turned around the man was gone. I got on the bus and the man with the knife was there …

Katie Brown (14)
John Masefield High School, Ledbury

Imagined Monster

I ran and I ran fast, but no matter how far and fast I ran, it was always nipping at my heels. That horrible sound, squelching, smacking sound, the muffled screams of its victims being digested. It got everyone, my family, my friends, who would have thought it, dangerous imagination!

Jed Parry (13)
John Masefield High School, Ledbury

Hanging There

I stood in the crowd crying for Grandma. The monster brought her out and placed the noose around her neck then the executioner pulled the lever. Her body shook violently; her eyes opened one second then closed. I screamed, the heavens opened then lightning struck her cold dead body.

Abbi Davies (13)
John Masefield High School, Ledbury

Clunk

Clunk! The trap sprung, the first wave of battalions were mown down like animals. The second wave was closing fast. They too were taken out with a volley of cannonballs. They were close now, there were apes hacking away at the turret. We would never get out, we were trapped!

David Benhenni (13)
John Masefield High School, Ledbury

181

The Greatest Day Of My Life

It was the greatest day ever. Hereford United were promoted to the Premiership and Swindon were relegated to the conference. It was the greatest day of my whole life. The legend Steve Guinan, the hat-trick hero. Hereford were in the Premiership for the first time in their great history.

Sam Keetch (13)
John Masefield High School, Ledbury

Daylight

It's finally here, daylight. It comes out, grabs the night with its hands and throws it as far as it can. The daylight over for another twelve hours. The people come out to do as much as they can in the twelve hours then the black night takes over.

Adam Perks (13)
John Masefield High School, Ledbury

183

Jetting

Jetting on the runway, going up and up in the sky.
The windows are shaking and the lights are flashing.
Seeing the clouds below us my stomach turns. My
ears are popping and are hurting a lot. The pilot
says our seatbelts are allowed off, I am suddenly so
excited.

Ellen Webb (13)
John Masefield High School, Ledbury

What Colour Would The Chameleon Change?

Near a fairground an inquisitive chameleon named Connie lived. She had decided to go to the fair. She wandered into a house of mirrors with chameleons changing to their surroundings. I wonder what colour she would change to.

Hayley Jones (13)
John Masefield High School, Ledbury

Trapped

As I was browsing through Somerfield, I noticed that it was deathly silent and heard a strange noise like a key being turned. I was trapped in Somerfield! How would I get out! I walked around looking for spare keys but there wasn't any! I decided to …

Jordan-Leigh Parry (13)
John Masefield High School, Ledbury

The Darkness

It's here, the black cloth, shadowed arms wrapping the world into total darkness. The fingers were moving speedily after me, clawing the ground and leaving only smoke as a trail, disappearing as quickly as the human race. The world of people has vanished; the end of the world has begun.

Nicholas Hetherington (12)
John Masefield High School, Ledbury

187

Corpse

I opened the door, it creaked all the way. I walked
in, there was a gush of wind, it was choking me. A
rat scurried across the floor, it gave me the shivers.
I made my way into the dusty living room. There
before me was my grandfather's rotten corpse!

Charlotte Febery (13)
John Masefield High School, Ledbury

At The Devil's Door

The distant sound of explosions rumbled through the murky air. Satan looked down the line of exhausted men, a haunted look in each one's eyes. He wondered how many of them were coming his way. Then, as a cold, shrill whistle sounded, they scrambled over the top of the trench.

Caitriona Cox (13)
King Williams' College, Isle of Man

The Cathedral

He hung onto the pillar. He saw the commotion down below, the organ swelling with the procession. He leapt onto a beam and prepared himself. His gun came out. The bellowing organ vibrated the rafters. He took aim, the man in robes sat on his throne, the assassin struck home.

Jenny Green (16)
King Williams' College, Isle of Man

The End

No man meets my eye. They look at sand already black with traitors' blood or at the woman whose weeping makes me wonder, will my unborn child cry like that? Chains contort my back like nightmares. 'Long live The Front!' I shout, yet still no man meets my eye.
'Fire!'

Kathryn Sharpe (15)
King Williams' College, Isle of Man

191

The Dog

I sat in a field with long grass and then I saw a
browny gingery terrier dog jump through the flowing
grass chasing sheep pretending to be a sheepdog.
Then, later when the sun came out she lay in the
grass falling asleep with her legs out like chicken
thighs!

Sophie White (13)
King Williams' College, Isle of Man

Island Champions

I was running as fast as I could, my stick was dragging behind me. I was getting closer to the goals, I struck the ball full power, it went through the goalie's legs. It hit the backboards, everyone was screaming. The final whistle went; we're the U13 Island Champions!

Sophie Van Hooven (13)
King Williams' College, Isle of Man

193

The Day I Almost Got Arrested But Didn't!

A policeman's at the door, oh no! Do they know about the bomb and rifle I'm building under my desk to plan to assassinate the neighbour's cat or the Cornetto I stole from the Co-op? 'I didn't do it,' I shouted.
'Good because the neighbour's chair's gone missing,' he replied.

Alex Beadle (14)
King Williams' College, Isle of Man

Rocks

Sarah poked her head into the rocky darkness of the cave. After a moment she slipped inside. I followed cautiously. My eyes took a minute to adjust to the gloom, but soon I made out the shapes of boulders.
No Sarah, then, *'Boo!'*
She nearly gave me a heart attack!

Harriet Nuttall (13)
King Williams' College, Isle of Man

No!

'No!' she screamed as the river pulled her hands away from the bank. She had jumped in to save her dog who had slipped in, he was now scrambling up the bank. She screamed again then her legs were grabbed by the invisible hands of Cold, slowly dragging her under.

Georgie Leece Drinkwater (13)
King Williams' College, Isle of Man

The Race Of Life

Adrenalin pumped Jeremy's veins as he surged forwards. It seemed that this was now, this was the moment, this was adventure as he felt his feet leave the edge of the cliff, he lifted his head to the wonderful freedom of the sky. It's just a shame lemmings can't fly.

Eleanor Leece Drinkwater (15)

King Williams' College, Isle of Man

The Chase

Silently the grey wolf crept. He was hiding in a bush. His prey, sensing someone there, darted the other way. The chase had then begun. The wolf had the advantage of being a quicker runner and soon caught up. He sank his dripping wet teeth savagely into his prey's throat.

Stephanie Carter (13)
King Williams' College, Isle of Man

Sue And The Chimp

Sue and the chimp went to the zoo to save chimp's friends. They crept past the enclosure, they reached the chimps. Sue got out her blowtorch and melted the iron cages. They grabbed the chimps and ran. They were being chased but they fell into the bear pit.

Jack Cooper (13)
King Williams' College, Isle of Man

199

Fate

'I don't want to live!' cried Chris.
'You don't mean that Chris,' retorted his mum
sympathetically.
'Yes I do, I'm gonna to kill myself!' screamed Chris.
Chris fled the house. That was the last time he was
seen, he got hit by a bus on his way to the cliffs.

Matt Kneen (13)
King Williams' College, Isle of Man

The Huge Jump

I'm going to risk it, risk everything. It's so high and I'm scared, below is just a blue blur. I'm wobbling; my feet are starting to slip. I'm getting butterflies in my stomach and there are hundreds of words running through my head. I will jump off this chair, *aargh!*

Grace Harrison (12)
King Williams' College, Isle of Man

Untitled

Splat! My heavy breathing rasped through my visor.
Thuck, thuck. I fired my gun. The adrenaline pumping
my heart thumping, crawling through the bushes,
I was lost in the game. The call, 'Attack!' Running,
diving to the ground. *Crack! Smack!* Hit in the face!
All for one game, paint balling.

Louis Schwalbert (14)
King Williams' College, Isle of Man

Slipping In The Darkness

I hung to the tree my life depended on it. My fingers were slipping. A caterpillar gently crawled across my fingers, its tiny hairs tickling them. I fell into the darkness. I landed with my hands still in the air. My feet were still were they always were, the ground.

Rowena Farrant (12)
King Williams' College, Isle of Man

Stay Calm

Two people, silence. They sat with me; one reached
into his pocket and peered around. A black long
shape sprung out. What was it?
'Stay calm, no one gets hurt.'
Screaming.
'Everyone down!'
Babies screaming, a smile across his face.
'Since who's afraid of a mouldy banana?'
Taking a bite.

Grace McCarthy (12)
Pattison College, Coventry

A Deserted Beach

A deserted beach, a surfboard, waves lapping around. Even the cliff café closing. My eyes search the sea; no one. I push out into the waves. Is he dead? A voice behind me, 'Hi, that's my board.' A blond guy in a lifeguard T-shirt. Holding a cup of tea.

Lucy Parker (12)

Roseberry School for Girls, Epsom

Untitled

I strolled down the beach, my feet sunk into the sand, beautiful scenery, perfect weather and the perfect boyfriend. I was on the way to see him; it was his birthday so I planned a surprise meal. I walked down the beach; he was with another girl, my best friend!

Georgina Goodgame (14)
St Mary's School, Gerrards Cross

To Fly

Slowly I get myself to the end of the branch. I look at my mom, then straight down, then I jump, flap my little wings and fall. The ground comes closer and closer, I hit the ground. 'Shall we try that again?' my mom asks. An hour later I flew!

Soffia Kristinsdottir (13)
St Mary's School, Gerrards Cross

The Scream

Walking along the beach in the light of day and I'm feeling entirely carefree and exceptionally happy. The sun's rays are hot and the breeze of the sea is cool. I then was alarmed by a scream of children crying in despair. Afterwards they shouted, 'You walked over our sandcastle!'

Hannah Beattie (13)
St Mary's School, Gerrards Cross

My Love

The first time I saw him I knew we were meant to be together. He was so handsome with long flowing hair. His eyes were brown and glittered mischievously. As I called his name he came running over. I smiled as he nuzzled my hand. I stroked my pony, Shandy.

Emily Patching (14)
St Mary's School, Gerrards Cross

209

Who Was There?

Alone I walked around the school, my occupation
being the caretaker. The night sky black, the air still,
nothing moving, just me, no one else. As I searched
the school, locking everything up, the pool water was
trembling, who was there?

Danielle Chauhan (14)
St Mary's School, Gerrards Cross

The Monster

The cave was dark and damp inside. Slowly an
emerald-green monster emerged from the shadows.
It approached me, gradually getting faster. I couldn't
decide if I should run or hide. I screamed and hid
behind a cushion, quickly turning the DVD player off.

Jeena Patel (14)
St Mary's School, Gerrards Cross

The Wire

He came closer with the metal wire in his hand reaching for me. My heart was thumping, I was shaking. He picked up a small metal pole. I felt the sharp edge touch me; the pain went through me … 'All done, your braces are on, you can leave now.'

Charlotte Grahame (14)
St Mary's School, Gerrards Cross

Go Away Dad!

Dad was holding my hand; I did not want him to go. I cried, it was my first day and I was only five. He had always held my hand. Why was he leaving me? He had never left me. Now I don't want him to get out the car.

Marie-Claire Gief (14)
St Mary's School, Gerrards Cross

Fifteen Years Ago

'I am your mother.' The words rang in her head.
Tears pricked in the young woman's icy stare. She
advanced towards her.
'Fifteen years and not a word,' she uttered, 'fifteen
years I have waited.'
'Fifteen years,' the young woman wept, 'is an awfully
long time to change.'

Megan Brown (14)
St Mary's School, Gerrards Cross

214

My Life Is Over

My life is over! Something that I'd spent hours working on is now broken! That wretched basketball and my annoyance of a little brother! I had spent 180 minutes choosing the perfect colour and the right gems and now it's over, my life is over, my nail is broken!

Prue Heywood (14)
St Mary's School, Gerrards Cross

Aeroplane

'Please fasten your seatbelt.' You could feel the excitement rushing through everyone. The first time flying was great, that is until the babies started crying, people started fighting, hundreds of people queuing for the toilet which stinks by the way! I fell asleep; the aeroplane began to take off.

Parisa Dezfuffi (14)
St Mary's School, Gerrards Cross

The Cottage Window

I felt a shudder as she walked past me, I waited, she stopped, stood still. She glimpsed through the distinct gap in the window of the small, lonesome cottage. Tears streamed down her perfect face and I knew she had seen what I had seen moments before her.

Jessica Cahill (14)
St Mary's School, Gerrards Cross

Struggle For Life

The bomb was ticking and she had to get out of the building. She ran down endless corridors in desperation as she looked for an exit from death. She saw a door that looked promising and flung it open wildly. It was the exit. She ran for her dear life.

Julia Wessels (13)
St Mary's School, Gerrards Cross

218

Boat To Spain

The wind was peacefully blowing and the waves crashing against the rocks, children laughing and splashing in the sea. The white boats scattered on the horizon of the sea as we got into the ship to be taken to Spain. People's stomachs churning and saying goodbye to their family.

Rachael Brooks (13)
St Mary's School, Gerrards Cross

The Loch Ness Monster

Oliver and Hugo were sitting down on a riverbank in Scotland one sunny day. There was a ripple in the water. 'Look over there,' Hugo cried quite interested, 'I wonder what it is.' A big dark scaly figure rose from the water.
'It is the monster, run!' Oliver screamed.

Rebekah Stokes (13)
St Mary's School, Gerrards Cross

As The Bell Rings!

I was running down the alleyway coming near the end. That face, those eyes flashing in my mind, those words falling in my ears.

'Don't be late!' Sweat and tears running down my face, my heart thumping under my jumper, that's when I heard the school bell ring.

Hannah Caraco (13)
St Mary's School, Gerrards Cross

221

Behind The Door

I made my way to the door. I was a little frightened.
As I opened the creaking door, I felt a gust of bitter
wind blow into my face. The door was wide and all
I saw was a flash. A bright flash which could blind
someone, it was Heaven.

Shereen Sagoo (13)
St Mary's School, Gerrards Cross

I Love Him

'I love him,' I shouted.
'You what?' my best friend said to me.
'Yeah, you heard me, I love him.' I ran out the room
wishing I could rewind time.
'What happened?' he said.
'I said our secret, well; they were going to know
some day. I definitely love you.'

Felicity Davis (13)
St Mary's School, Gerrards Cross

The Nightmare

I could hear him; his echoing laugh filled every nook and cranny of the abandoned cave. I could see the light. I could feel him now. His sharp claws digging into the back of my head. The blood dripped down from my hair onto my coat. It stopped, he'd vanished!

Tara Hurst (13)
St Mary's School, Gerrards Cross

The Big News

I was at home having tea and then my parents told me they were getting a divorce. I ran as far away as possible. I went to my friend's house; she said I could stay the night. I picked up my bags and stepped into a house of doom, uh-oh!

Lucy Marshall (12)
St Mary's School, Gerrards Cross

Cliffhanger

My life flashed before my eyes. Everything became clear, I'd made a mistake. I pulled myself up, my fingers digging into the rock. One hand slipped and I was forced to look down. It wasn't supposed to end this way but the pain was unbearable, I had to let go.

Tara Manjunath (13)
Sutton Coldfield Grammar School for Girls, Sutton Coldfield

The Chase

My heart thudded violently. I could hear the distant screams, it was approaching fast. I stumbled and tripped. I had to keep on running or it would get me. Rustling sounds came from the bush; it was there right in front of me. I had lost the game of tig.

Afeaza Raheef (13)
Sutton Coldfield Grammar School for Girls, Sutton Coldfield

The Magic Moon

Here I was on the moon. How was I even breathing? How could I even walk? I kicked a small rock, it flew through the air. *Just me then,* I thought. This wasn't the first time. I must stop going to that place, I must stop activating The Doomed PlayStation.

Frances Hancock (13)
Sutton Coldfield Grammar School for Girls, Sutton Coldfield

Never-Ending

It was pitch-black as no glowing stars could be seen. There was no escape. The willows waved and cracked in the harsh wind. I could hear the river roar nearby as thunder clapped. As I ran towards the golden key it seemed further and further away. A never-ending world!

Ajit Kaur Sagoo (13)
Sutton Coldfield Grammar School for Girls, Sutton Coldfield

Pain

I had never seen anything like it. I opened my mouth, no sound came out. The screaming was echoing in my ears and I tried to run but couldn't. Blood, screaming, and tears running down their cheeks. I didn't even notice the bullet until it was too late.

Laura Sumner (13)

Sutton Coldfield Grammar School for Girls, Sutton Coldfield

The Building

Driving up the road and climbing out of the car.
The tall people walking past staring down at me.
The large rooms roaring with sound and people
screaming. A strange looking woman came over to
me. She looked at me with a cold hard stare ... my
first day at school.

Imogen Paffister (13)
Sutton Coldfield Grammar School for Girls, Sutton Coldfield

The Race

Running, running, I can't stop, away from the dreaded people. As my heart pumps faster they are coming up behind me. I can hear screams, feet pounding near me. I can see green grass in front of me, nobody else next to me. I am alone. At my first sports day.

Diana Shiner (12)
Sutton Coldfield Grammar School for Girls, Sutton Coldfield

Disaster

The dark, gloomy night had just got worse. The flooding had now killed five people and left eleven people unconscious. It was thundering and the rain had got even heavier. It was horrendous. All of the banks had burst and the floods had reached six feet. England was being destroyed!

Anjeevan Kfair (13)
Sutton Coldfield Grammar School for Girls, Sutton Coldfield

Untitled

She sits there staring into space, her mind scanning for ideas, nearly reaching bursting point. Lost, confused, thinking deeper and deeper hoping to find something special and unique. A vast clear white space lay before her worried eyes, her heart flutters as the teacher asks to see her work.

Chloe Scott (13)
Sutton Coldfield Grammar School for Girls, Sutton Coldfield

Guilt

Hands sweating, heart thumping, tears rolling down my face, butterflies in my stomach, teeth chattering, nose running, dark squashed, gloomy room. Teachers glaring at me with shame, pressure rising rapidly, trying to think about something, reflecting over my bad sin. Slowly breathing deeply in and out, my first ever detention.

Sarah Rehman (13)
Sutton Coldfield Grammar School for Girls, Sutton Coldfield

It Makes Me Wonder

Round they go, from dawn until dusk. Hands reach out to me from every direction. So much time, but time stays the same. Some are lifeless, twitching slightly. I can't help feeling like I'm being watched. It makes me wonder how much time I have. Here in the clock shop.

Anna Owen (13)

Sutton Coldfield Grammar School for Girls, Sutton Coldfield

The Final Sin

Crying, the sweet little girl lay in bed apologising to herself and praying for forgiveness. It was only midday, she heard people laughing but she thought this crime was unforgivable. Little did she know that this crime wasn't illegal, in fact, a little girl eating a Yorkie is completely acceptable.

Laura Buff (12)
Sutton Coldfield Grammar School for Girls, Sutton Coldfield

The Calling

Rose muttered curses under her breath as she picked
her way through the thorns. She looked up, it was a
full moon, she let out a yelp of surprise and picked up
her pace ignoring the sweat trickling into her eyes.
Finally she reached the sea, home and plunged in.

Chloé Thompson-Haynes (13)
Sutton Coldfield Grammar School for Girls, Sutton Coldfield

My Final Jump

The world swerved up and down ferociously, my vision blurred as I carried on. I began to lose my breath, slower and slower. I couldn't stop now, I've come too far. Can't help it! It's just too hard. Out of breath I climbed off my ten-foot trampoline.

Shannan Cox (12)
Sutton Coldfield Grammar School for Girls, Sutton Coldfield

Emotions Within

The sparkle in their eyes had gone. Their personalities had changed. Souls destroyed, emotions disappeared but they were still his friends and even though they never talked to him or noticed him anymore they were still there. He wasn't alone, he was happy in his house of corpses.

Laurel Windsor (13)

Sutton Coldfield Grammar School for Girls, Sutton Coldfield

Reflections

Symmetrical left to right, back to front, it all looked the same in my eye. I could make a few of the features out, a pair of eyes, a nose, an ear and a patch of glistening black hair spiralling outwards. It reminds me of someone familiar … oh yes, me!

Jamilah Campbell (13)
Sutton Coldfield Grammar School for Girls, Sutton Coldfield

241

The Best Gift

Pacing up and down the narrow white corridor, his
mind racing. So many thoughts all pounding in his
head. His palms starting to sweat, suspense lay heavy
in the air. A door opened and he was called in, he
was greeted by two big blue eyes.
His little baby girl.

Charlotte Baxter (12)

Sutton Coldfield Grammar School for Girls, Sutton Coldfield

The Birthday Party

The tinsel sparkling in my eyes, my heart pounding to the rhythm of the beat, the party poppers hitting the ceiling like bombs. I hear the sound of voices singing as they bring in the cake. My lips watering and in seconds, *splat!* The cake was all over my face.

Aisha Kafeem (13)
Sutton Coldfield Grammar School for Girls, Sutton Coldfield

243

The Apocalypse

My belly filling with butterflies, my friends all
screaming with fear. My insides feel like jelly,
looking down gives me shivers. Holding tight, hands
becoming sweaty. Eyes shut until we reached the
top – I peeked, saw a wonderful view. Then he said,
'Three ... two ... one. '
And we're down, it's over!

Nafeesa Mehmood (13)
Sutton Coldfield Grammar School for Girls, Sutton Coldfield

The White Flag Flies

Wearing shorts and flippers he dived in. The cold was so powerful; it turned his body blue with numbness. He bobbed up and down for a while until he saw the white flag fly from far on the port. He turned around and came face to face with its teeth.

Anmol Hussain (13)
Sutton Coldfield Grammar School for Girls, Sutton Coldfield

245

Taking A Plunge

The liquid below me whirled and bubbled. I shivered as a hand reached out and held me on the edge. My heart pumped as I plummeted into the freezing depths below me. I struggled and gasped as I tried desperately to reach the surface. My first swimming lesson.

Ciara Ryan (13)

Sutton Coldfield Grammar School for Girls, Sutton Coldfield

Terror

In the darkness, not alone, the echoes of ghastly
screams rebound off the hollow surfaces, haunting
laughs repeatedly travelling through my head.
Struck with terror my jaw fell open as unexpected
faces started smiling out of nowhere. My stomach
churning, the doors opening, rushing thoughts, light
appearing, the ride's finished.

Sheffy Rajput (13)
Sutton Coldfield Grammar School for Girls, Sutton Coldfield

247

A Race For Life

The man loomed closer, he took out the gun. He aimed, he shot. All I could think about was the noise, my body jerked in convulsions; I was gliding, further and further away from the man. I was floating on air … the burning sensation slowly diminished, I won the 100m.

Catherine White (14)

Sutton Coldfield Grammar School for Girls, Sutton Coldfield

The Morning After The Night Before

Noise flooded my empty house as people rushed in gripping stereos and alcohol. I don't recall inviting all these people, strangers jumping on furniture, cigarette burns on the sofa. Havoc emerged, on the floor lay smashed ornaments and empty bottles. That night they had fun.
Today I will be punished!

Sarah Lyons (14)
Sutton Coldfield Grammar School for Girls, Sutton Coldfield

White Wedding

Plucking up all of my courage, I stood, I spoke. The
congregation startled and in disbelief, slowly turned
their penetrating gaze to me. I took a step forward.
'He is already married!' I spoke with nerves shaking.
The tall groom turned puzzlement across his face.
It was the wrong wedding!

Sarah Hemming (14)
Sutton Coldfield Grammar School for Girls, Sutton Coldfield

Cinderella's Saga

All of those mice, the pumpkin, this meringue dress
and he didn't even look at me once. Even my nails
and hair had taken hours too! In anger I kicked off
one of those stupid slippers which shattered noisily.
Oh well, it wasn't as if he would even find it!

Elizabeth Parry (14)
Sutton Coldfield Grammar School for Girls, Sutton Coldfield

An Ordinary Day At The Pool

Hurrying round, gathering my swimming gear, as my
mind began to wander.
'Focus!' I told myself, 'you'll forget something later.'
I emerged from the pool, cold and wet. I stood
motionless after frantically rummaging through my
bag. I had forgotten my underwear. Oh great, yet
another extremely uncomfortable journey home.

Kate Densley (14)
Sutton Coldfield Grammar School for Girls, Sutton Coldfield

Tinnitus

I woke up, the constant ringing of bells in my ears again. I open the window wide and breathe in cool, fresh air, the bells neither louder nor quieter. In frustration, I push my fingers into my ears to no avail. I knew I shouldn't have played music so loud.

Eleanor Smithson (14)
Sutton Coldfield Grammar School for Girls, Sutton Coldfield

Untitled

They're running from me. They can see the knife.
One stumbles, my sister, I lunge at her writhing body,
intentionally stabbing her heart, her crimson blood
spilling out of the gaping hole. I hear a scream and
wake to find it my own, staring at the knife in my
hand.

Nicola Swafes (14)
Sutton Coldfield Grammar School for Girls, Sutton Coldfield

The Noise

Ellie sat still, listening intently to the noise downstairs.
Who was there? She stole down the stairs, crept
along the hall, sneaked into the lounge and watched
an intruder lift her television into a crate. The second
he spotted Ellie she was plunged into a world of
darkness and terror.

Rhia Abukhalil (12)
Sutton Coldfield Grammar School for Girls, Sutton Coldfield

Aliens

It all started when Alex and I were walking home from school. It was almost dusk; we knew we were going to be late because we missed the bus. As we turned the corner, out came a flying saucer. I looked up and saw that Alex was gone forever.

Noor Hashim Hussain (11)
Sutton Coldfield Grammar School for Girls, Sutton Coldfield

Moving On

Emily lived in Cornwall and collected pebbles. On Friday, Emily walked to the beach and gathered some. The tide came in and swept Emily onto rocks. She got up and climbed to safety. Emily arrived home; her mother was ringing the coastguard! Then Emily realised she herself, had moved on.

Charlotte Dixon (12)
Sutton Coldfield Grammar School for Girls, Sutton Coldfield

Shadows

A year ago, I was walking through the moonlit woods, amongst the mist clinging to the ghostly branches, alone, when a white light shone from amongst the wilderness, then shadowed figures began drifting towards me. They whispered in hushed phrases the words I shall never forget. 'The end is near.'

Bethany Holt (12)
Sutton Coldfield Grammar School for Girls, Sutton Coldfield

The 18th Hole

'He has to make this shot,' whispered a spectator.
'Quiet please, on the 18th tee.'
Tiger Woods looking nervously, only one shot away
from the winner. The spectator had his camera ready
dawdling by the green. Tiger swung but before he
could say, 'shot' he was down like a bullet.

Hayley Prichard-Jones (12)
Sutton Coldfield Grammar School for Girls, Sutton Coldfield

Captured

I have nowhere to go now, no hope, nothing. I don't
have the strength to talk or even move. I should
have stayed away. I shouldn't' have fought with him.
Captured, I know it, but it had to be done, I had to
save the boy. He's safe, I'm not.

Dayna Hiff (12)

Sutton Coldfield Grammar School for Girls, Sutton Coldfield

The Journey

'Are we there yet?'
'No!' Dad replied.
'Are we there yet?'
'This is the eleventh time you have asked me that, no!'
'I can't wait to go on Apocalypse and Shockwave and Maelstrom. It's going to be such fun. Dad, I know you're going to shout but are we there?'

Serena Chandra (12)
Sutton Coldfield Grammar School for Girls, Sutton Coldfield

The House

I strolled along the pavement of Church Lane. I came
to a stop, there was a house, an old church. I walked
inside eagerly. It was spooky. I tiptoed up the stairs
shaking. A noise travelled to my ears. A dark figure
was in front, that night, my life ended.

Chloé Upston (12)
Sutton Coldfield Grammar School for Girls, Sutton Coldfield

High House

The old shutters banged against the broken windows in the wind. The moon beamed onto the roof, the tiles revealed the house's age. Something scuttled across my foot. The house stood proud. They had said, whoever had entered the house never lived to tell the tale, I entered the house …

Affie Hexfey (12)
Sutton Coldfield Grammar School for Girls, Sutton Coldfield

One Wish

My birthday! I can make a wish, will it come true?
The cake is jam sponge with white icing and coloured
balloons as decoration. The candles are lit, glistening
brightly. I hear 'Happy Birthday' nearly time to blow
out the candles. I'm racking my brains, the moment
of truth, wish!

Charlotte Heath (12)
Sutton Coldfield Grammar School for Girls, Sutton Coldfield

The Shadows

At 9.30 I am in bed. Dark, roaring thunder and lightning. My eyes half-closed with fright, I saw shadows on the wall. The shadows dance, the wind howls outside. A cold chill runs over me. I slowly bury myself in my duvet, I open my eyes, it's morning.

Vanisha Chauhan (12)
Sutton Coldfield Grammar School for Girls, Sutton Coldfield

The Announcement

'Mum, I'm nervous,' I said.
'Don't be, it will be fine.'
I stepped in front of the class shaking a little.
'I will not be in Year 8 with you because as you know
my sister is going to University in Canada and so am
I.'
There was silence.

Megan Kirby (12)
Sutton Coldfield Grammar School for Girls, Sutton Coldfield

Red Rum

I blew on the cold glass window. Condensation dripped onto the frame. Without thinking I drew his name on it with my finger.
Suddenly I was outside, looking in. I realised what I had written: *Murder*. In an instant, I heard a scream and was plunged into eternal darkness.

Grace Davis (12)
Sutton Coldfield Grammar School for Girls, Sutton Coldfield

Murder In The Dark

I ran like I was being chased by a mass murderer, little did I know how true these words were. The nearby river glistened in the moonlight, the dark night's sky made it impossible to see in front. I stopped, I screamed, the light faded and never came back.

Amber Cruise (12)
Sutton Coldfield Grammar School for Girls, Sutton Coldfield

268

Thief

Stealthily David crept along the carpet that led to wooden doors. The moon shone through the window, but David did not worry, everyone was asleep. He tiptoed into a bedroom. He took all of the valuables. Suddenly a baby's crying was heard. Someone woke up. David froze, he was caught!

Stephanie Sam (12)
Sutton Coldfield Grammar School for Girls, Sutton Coldfield

Don't Laugh At A Witch

There was once an obnoxious girl who had golden locks. One day she met an ugly witch and started to laugh at her. The witch got very angry and uttered a spell which caused the girl's tongue to drop off. The villagers were very happy and lived happily ever after.

Hajrah Zafar (12)
Sutton Coldfield Grammar School for Girls, Sutton Coldfield

Lovely Nights

She went over to him, as he was lying on his bed she stroked his soft brown hair, twisting it around in her hand. She kissed him on his head and told him about her day. She leaned in to hug him. 'You're the best dog ever Scruff,' she said.

Jasmin Beckford (12)
Sutton Coldfield Grammar School for Girls, Sutton Coldfield

The Unknown Search

She searched through all the cupboards.
She knew he was coming.
She scurried through all of her belongings,
when suddenly she could hear movement coming
from beneath the floor.
He was here!
She began to panic, losing valuable energy.
She turned around …
'Have you found the car keys?' he said.

Priya Padham (12)
Sutton Coldfield Grammar School for Girls, Sutton Coldfield

272

Fire In The Garden

It was so hot all you could see was the heat rising;
the smoke was covering the whole garden. You
could smell burning miles away. Loads of people
were coughing badly. A few people came to see what
was happening but we said everything was fine. The
sausages were burnt.

Charanveer Mudher (12)
Sutton Coldfield Grammar School for Girls, Sutton Coldfield

273

Love On The Balcony

He gazed into her eyes and she gazed into his eyes
on the balcony of their hotel suite, daydreaming into
each other's eyes. He went to kiss her on the cheek
but suddenly took hold of her shoulder, sat her on
the balcony and pushed her off to die painfully.

Devinia Solanki (11)

Sutton Coldfield Grammar School for Girls, Sutton Coldfield

274

Footsteps

To hide, the girl shivered in her hiding place. She tried to keep her racing heart under control but it thumped against her ribs thunderously. Suddenly she heard footsteps, he was in the room! In the wardrobe, the girl's heart leapt. The doors opened. 'I've found you, it's my turn!'

Charlotte Ridout (12)
Sutton Coldfield Grammar School for Girls, Sutton Coldfield

The Scene

She knew she had to escape from the kidnappers.
She ran and ran, running for her life. Her eyes
scanning the trees searching for her love, she had
found him running towards him, she stopped realising
he was shot!
'Cut!' shouted the director.
After all, it was a film.

Shaista Malik (12)

Sutton Coldfield Grammar School for Girls, Sutton Coldfield

Love At First Sight

He lifted her up in his arms and she smiled deeply into his eyes. Love was in the air definitely. 'I love you,' she whispered as she leaned on his shoulder and looked into the distance. He could smell her scent, she ran to hug a bear selling balloons.

Anisa Hawa (12)
Sutton Coldfield Grammar School for Girls, Sutton Coldfield

Alone In The Hotel Room

She was alone in the hotel room when she heard a knock-knock at the door. She quietly crept over in the dark and slowly turned the door handle. As she opened the door with a quivering hand she heard a rattle. She peeped around and saw … room service.

Nicole Parsons (12)
Sutton Coldfield Grammar School for Girls, Sutton Coldfield

Smooth Criminal

Little Lucy bounded up to an old man in Beatties.
'Excuse me, I can't find my mummy.'
'It's OK little girl, go and tell the cashier and she'll help you.'
Lucy ran over to the cashier and bought a box of jelly babies with the man's money she'd just stolen!

Amy Curry (12)
Sutton Coldfield Grammar School for Girls, Sutton Coldfield

First Love

He felt her golden shimmering hair and gazed deeply into her crystal blue eyes. The sea lapped gently up the soft Californian sand covering their feet with a warm clear liquid. Under the sunset she wrapped her arms around his body. He sobbed; first murder was forever the hardest thing.

Caryss Jones (11)
Sutton Coldfield Grammar School for Girls, Sutton Coldfield

Triggered Love

The lagoon glistened silver in the brilliant light of the moon. Sarah gazed at David and saw his grey eyes shine in loving reply. She pulled him into her arms and held him for a while then whispered softly, 'I'm sorry.' And produced her pistol then pulled back the trigger.

Bethan Renwick (12)

Sutton Coldfield Grammar School for Girls, Sutton Coldfield

Guardian Of Skies

Riding through the sky on her unicorn, pure and white, the wind flying through her hair, smiling happily, she gazed over the world. Bright colours lit up her face; she could hear music roaming like a guardian protecting all. She and her unicorn got struck by lightning and dropped dead.

Kirpaf Sagoo (12)

Sutton Coldfield Grammar School for Girls, Sutton Coldfield

282

Secrets

They were listening to the calming sound of the violins as they ate their candlelit dinner in peace. When suddenly Mark told Lucy he had a secret to share. Lucy was intrigued to see what Mark's secret was but she was surprised when Mark revealed his bright green glowing face!

Constance Martin (12)
Sutton Coldfield Grammar School for Girls, Sutton Coldfield

283

The Voice

Melanie had stayed late at school and was walking home on an icy, cold, dark, misty December evening. She felt scared stiff. Suddenly, a hand grabbed her shoulder. Mother's voice said, 'I came to meet you, I thought you might be scared.'
Melanie laughed, 'What me? You must be joking!'

Stephanie Doswell (12)

Sutton Coldfield Grammar School for Girls, Sutton Coldfield

Candlelit Dinner

They sat at the table in a small romantic corner with the candle lit. He pulled out a beautiful sweet smelling rose as her eyes watered. Suddenly he pressed the button on the stem and he shot the bullet then he whispered into his mic that he'd accomplished his mission.

Maaria Ashraf (12)
Sutton Coldfield Grammar School for Girls, Sutton Coldfield

285

The Frightful Child

I noticed a man I'd never seen before striking my mother. I gathered my weapons from my room. As he entered he had a shiny object behind his back. She was crying so I bashed through the door. I spotted a ring on her finger for the first time.

Efin Lee (12)
Sutton Coldfield Grammar School for Girls, Sutton Coldfield

Cliff Top Romance

They decided to go for a walk, the area was lovely
and mountainous, the sea was nearby. They went
to get a better view from the top of a nearby cliff.
They gazed into the others eyes with the sea making
peaceful noises, then she pushed him off the cliff.

Hannah Skelding (12)
Sutton Coldfield Grammar School for Girls, Sutton Coldfield

Dinner For Two

There they sat around the candlelit table in the Italian restaurant enjoying a meal of spaghetti. They sat gazing into each other's eyes and laughing at each other's jokes. He leant over the middle of the table, put his mouth by her ear and whispered, 'Thanks for coming Mom!'

Megan Rowley (12)
Sutton Coldfield Grammar School for Girls, Sutton Coldfield

Safari Attack

I continued through the Savannah to find water, my bare feet burning on the ground. I was nearly there. I carried on in the scorching sun. Behind me I heard something so I turned and before me stood a huge lion. He bounded towards me and licked my right foot.

Jeevan Gogna (12)
Sutton Coldfield Grammar School for Girls, Sutton Coldfield

What Am I?

I feel all gloopy and sticky. I'm as brown as a chocolate bar. Someone is putting me in a container. I'm thrust into a cage, it's boiling hot, I'm bubbling up and rising.

After twenty minutes of torture someone brings me out.

I am a cake!

Lily Westerman (11)
The Buchan School, Isle of Man

Should I Risk It?

Sprinting around the corner I find a bus heading my way. Dragging myself into an alley, I hear screeching motorbikes. I glance down at my leg; a twisted ankle! Should I risk it for the chocolate button across the road in Lego City? No other hamster has made it alive!

Sarah Butler (11)
The Buchan School, Isle of Man

291

Backstabber

In the dusty moonlight a girl sits in the shadows,
watching her best friend walk home. As she passes,
the girl reluctantly follows. Shaking, she carries a
sharp knife behind her back. Silent tears fall from her
bloodshot eyes, 'I'm sorry,' she cries and plunges the
knife through her back.

Yasmin & Sam
Varndean School, Brighton

Cheat

It was a warm evening, the sun going down, perfect.
I walk towards Oliver; I grab my knife from my
pocket.
'Hey babe,' he says unaware of his fate.
'I saw you with Michelle kissing, we're over.' I raise
the knife to his chest and stab him. 'I'm sorry.'

Emma Hodges
Varndean School, Brighton

Blood Footsteps

He placed his hands on the driving wheel and started the engine. The car jolted as the shaky engine propelled forward. No one knew he was capable of it. He got out the car after a few minutes and walked towards the bushes. His blood covered footsteps stomped the grass.

Julia Knight
Varndean School, Brighton

294

That Guy

We met online. He sounded nice; we had a lot in
common. He asked to meet so there we were, I
wanted to break the silence but he did first. We went
back to his house, he told me to turn off my phone
and from his pocket he drew …

Sophie Hyland-Ward
Varndean School, Brighton

Dark Night

Once upon a dreaded thought, an unthinkable crime to murder an innocent person. Shamus was walking home from high school when a dark figure appeared in front of him down a pitch-black alley. He panicked and with fright immediately ran the other way. As soon as he got home he locked all the doors in his house and then …

Bradley Mitten
Varndean School, Brighton

Cold December

It was in that night, the night of my father's death.
I heard a noise, a noise I had never heard before.
It was like a cry for help. I ran downstairs, there
was blood dripping everywhere. What could have
happened? Was it my dad?
I never saw him again.

Amy Jenner (13)
Varndean School, Brighton

The Lift

He stared through the small window. Looking dreamily at the brand new PS3, it was just sitting there mocking him. If only he could take it, maybe he could. There were no guards or staff looking so he walked in and grabbed it. Should he or shouldn't he have lifted?

Callum Clark (13)
Varndean School, Brighton

The Ghostly Child

The wooden swing swung motionless from the willow tree. The woman watched as a young girl climbed upon it and began swinging. The woman looked away for a split second then looked back. The swing was motionless and the girl was gone. Where was she in the vast open field?

Alice Woodings (13)
Varndean School, Brighton

299

The Dogfight

Wing Commander Gibbs walked down the airfield, his heart beating like a high tempo drumbeat. Sure enough he'd flown before the war, quite good at it, but never did he think he'd be a combat pilot. He feared for his life, what if he lost in a forthcoming dogfight?

Charlie Pullen
Varndean School, Brighton

The Alley

Once upon a cold windy day, when the tree excludes the leaves, three children named Ben, Kieran and Davis were walking down a quiet and lonely alley when they were attacked by a werewolf with a chainsaw under his belt. They all got brutally murdered.

Kieran Benn
Varndean School, Brighton

301

Centous And The Wingman

Once upon a time there was a young man called
Centous and a beat called Wingman. Wingman was
evil and Centous was good. Wingman was killing
people of Goole so Centous went, pulled out his
super sword and killed Wingman. Centous and Goole
lived happily ever after.

Kayne Hyde (14)
Vermuyden School, Goole

Spartan

In a dark area there was a man named The Spartan. He is on a journey to retrieve a spear called The Spear of Achilles. He is very mad about The Spartan in his area so Achilles set off to find The Spartan and brutally slit his neck.

Daniel West (13)
Vermuyden School, Goole

Killer Dog

Once upon a time there was a hero called Billy. He was a very wise man who helped everyone but one day an old woman arrived in the village and started killing people. She killed them because she and her dog could only survive on blood.

Brea Walton (14)
Vermuyden School, Goole

Road To Glory

Gabriel pushed the beast away with his shield then slashed it with the rusty old blade on the sword. He took one more big swing at the skinny looking neck of the beast and cut it clean off, with blood just simply squirting out of the upper torso.

Ben Evans (14)
Vermuyden School, Goole

Information

We hope you have enjoyed reading this book - and that you will continue to enjoy it in the coming years.

If you like reading and writing, drop us a line or give us a call and we'll send you a free information pack. Alternatively visit our website at www.youngwriters.co.uk

Write to:
Young Writers Information,
Remus House,
Coltsfoot Drive,
Peterborough,
PE2 9JX
Tel: (01733) 890066
Email: youngwriters@forwardpress.co.uk